JIM BORGMAN

Disturbing the Peace

Introduction by
Bill Watterson

Back cover photo by Robert A. Flischel

Special thanks, as always, to
The Cincinnati Enquirer

King Features Syndicate

and the production team at
The Merten Company

Published by
Colloquial Books
P.O. 20045
Cincinnati, Ohio 45220

ISBN: 0-9609632-5-1
Library of Congress Catalog Card Number: 95-71601

For Dylan and Chelsea,

with thanks for all the
Happy Girls and Dinosaurs

Other Books by Jim Borgman:

Smorgasborgman
The Great Communicator
The Mood of America
(with James F. McCarty)
Jim Borgman's Cincinnati

Introduction

I saw my first Jim Borgman cartoon almost twenty years ago. I went to Kenyon College just after Jim graduated from there and had been hired by *The Cincinnati Enquirer.* Jim's collegiate and professional cartoons so impressed me that I decided to become an editorial cartoonist myself. Jim encouraged my early efforts, critiquing my work and offering advice throughout my college years. This flattered me into pursuing a career for which I had neither the brains nor the talent. That ruined several years of my life, and I still hold Jim responsible for it.

Fate loves a good joke, and upon my graduation, I was hired to be Jim's rival across town at *The Cincinnati Post.* In the few months it took my editor to realize I was a complete fraud, I had the opportunity to study Jim's cartoons every morning. As my cartoon ideas were systematically rejected, I looked to Jim's work in dumb amazement for answers. How did he think of that one? How did he think to draw it that way? I could see where he had gone, but the path eluded me completely. If I hadn't been run out of Cincinnati so quickly, I'm sure I'd have grown to despise his immense talent.

Since those days, Jim's work has only gotten better. After ten or twenty years, most cartoonists sink into predictable routines, plopping each subject into reliable formulas. Their opinions bore and their craft stagnates. Jim's cartoons, however, seem to develop greater subtlety and sophistication every year. He somehow adds new layers of reflection, insight and personality to his work, and makes it all look effortless under that wonderful draftsmanship.

Boy, can Jim draw. The bold compositions, the lively caricatures, the odd perspective, the imaginative distortions—this is a cartoonist who takes full advantage of his medium. Jim's sharply observed and intimate domestic scenes delight me no end. That picture of the woman hopping around, trying to get into her jeans is one I'd love to have drawn myself. I love the obese dog, the hausfrau in stretch pants, the glass of wine on the floor, the cardigan sweaters, the peculiar artifacts on the bookshelves, the kitchen clutter, the kid about to pound away on the piano. These things are all around us, but it's the rare cartoonist who notices and can present them with such honesty and silly affection.

Which brings me pretty much back to where I started in 1976, marveling at what this guy can do with ink and paper. Look at these cartoons, and you'll marvel, too. But take it from me, it's nowhere near as easy as Jim makes it look.

BILL WATTERSON, 1995

Bill Watterson is the creator of "Calvin and Hobbes."

SCIENTISTS LOCATE THE JEANS
LOCATING THE OBESITY JEANS
COME IN IT'S COOL INSIDE
"THE HECK WITH THIS 'DOG DAYS' CRA
ACCOUNTS RECEIVABLE
" JUST HOW LONG DO YOU PROPOSE TO 'EASE BACK IN' FROM VACATION, SMAGARINSKY ?"
" LOOKS LIKE KLINGLER'S TUNED IN TO Z-ROCK AGAIN... "
When did the FAX MACHINE IS A TOASTER
WOODSTOCK '94
THE 25TH ANNIVERSARY
PEOPLE, WE HAVE REPORTS OF SOME BAD

My G-G-Generation

10/11/92

CHRISTOPHER COLUMBUS, YOU'VE HAD 500 YEARS TO PONDER YOUR INVASION OF AMERICA. YOUR THOUGHTS.
SHAPE-A LIKE-A EGG. ASSA ALL I WASSA TRYING TO PROVE...
BANGOR
MILWAUKEE
DISEASE, PESTILENCE, GENOCIDE, THE TOMAHAWK CHOP... REGRETS?
A TRADE ROUTE— HONEST TO GOD! THASSA ALL I WAS...
ETHNIC CLEANSING, 1492. YOUR REACTION.
TEA... SPICES... MAYBE A GOOD CUP OF COFFEE....
JIM BORGMAN CINCINNATI ENQUIRER ©92
LET'S GO TO THE PHONES.... WOUNDED KNEE, SOUTH DAKOTA, YOU'RE ON WITH CHRISTOPHER COLUMBUS...
NEXT TIME I ONLY DO RUSH LIMBAUGH.

1/11/94

"I STILL DON'T THINK WE'VE QUITE GOT IT, SIR...."

5/4/92

"ACTUALLY, HARRY IS SOMETHING OF AN AUTHORITY ON THE FOOD PYRAMID HIMSELF......"

12/8/94

JIM BORGMAN
CINCINNATI ENQUIRER ©1994
Great Moments in Science:
LOUISE ZUCKER LOCATES THE JEANS ASSOCIATED WITH WEIGHT GAIN

7/7/92

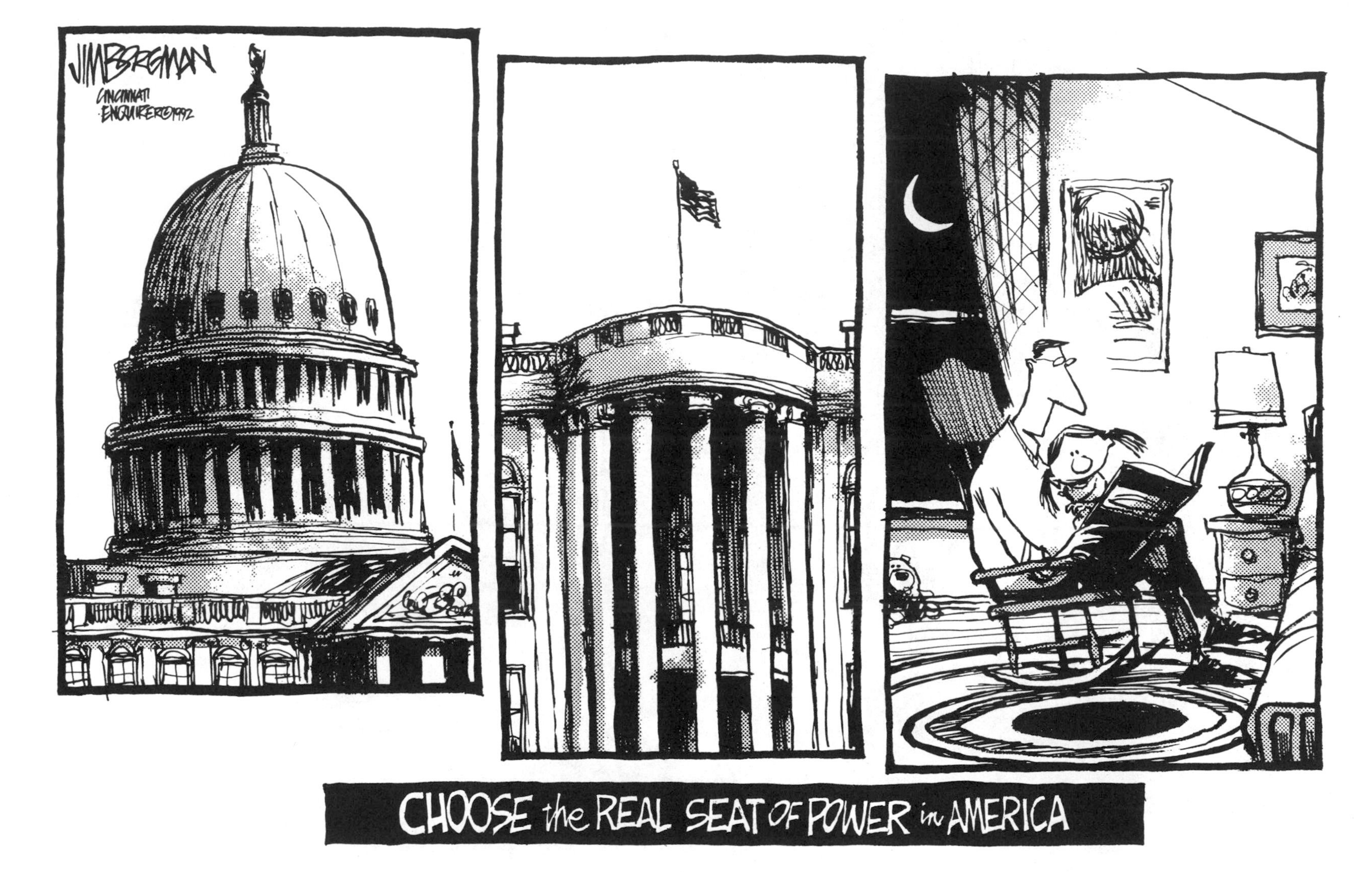
JIM BORGMAN
CINCINNATI ENQUIRER©1992
CHOOSE the REAL SEAT OF POWER in AMERICA

1/5/92

IF YOU GIVE
A MAN A FISH,
HE WILL EAT
FOR A DAY.
IF YOU TEACH
A MAN TO FISH,
HE WILL EAT FOR
A LIFETIME.
IF YOU TEACH A CHILD TO FISH,
HE MAY
FEED THE WORLD.
JIM BORGMAN
©92 The CINCINNATI ENQUIRER

1/26/87

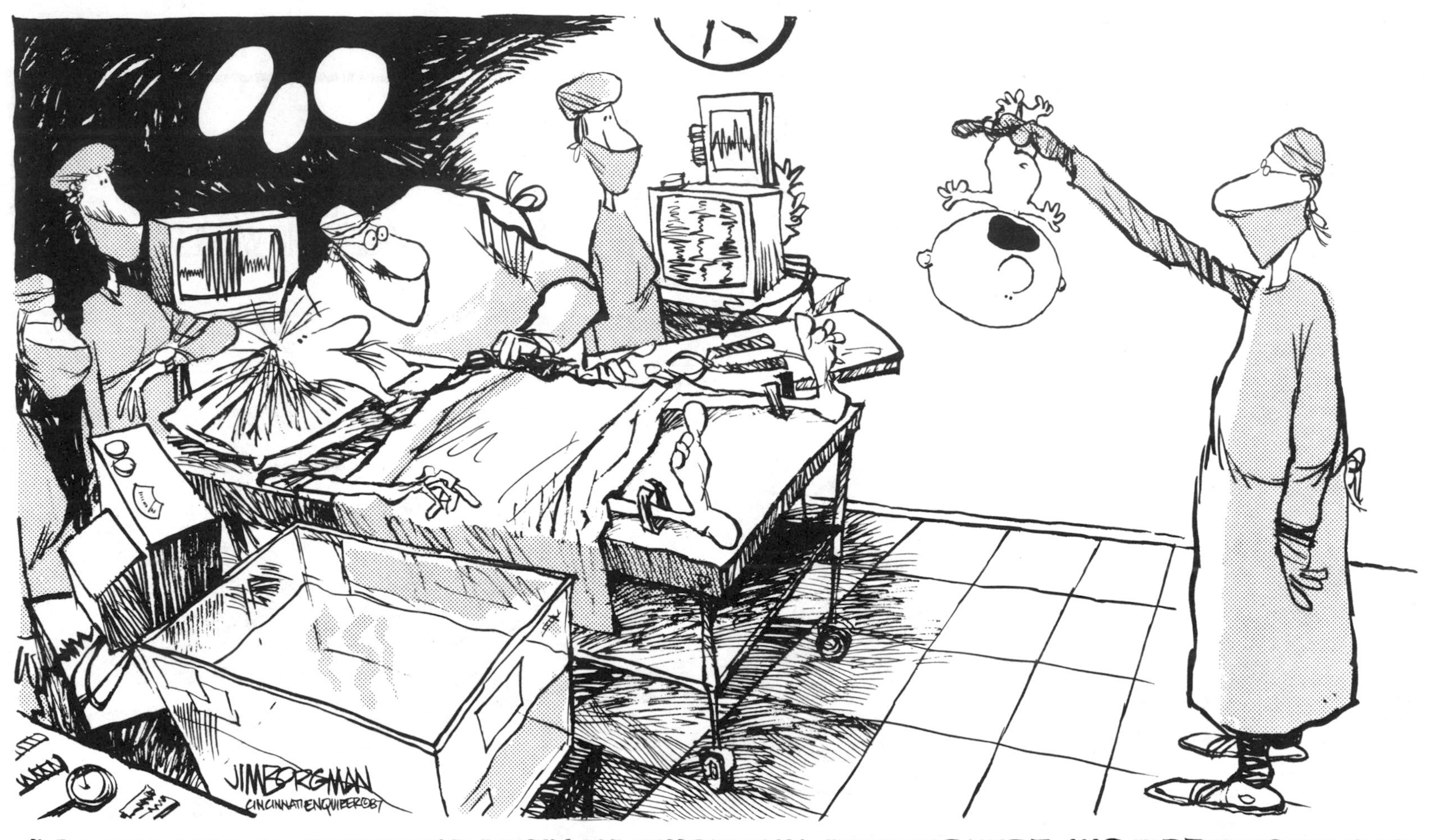

"SO TELL ME, DOC, BEFORE WE BEGIN ANY EMOTIONAL BONDING HERE: HAS IT BEEN ESTABLISHED WHO MY LEGAL PARENTS ARE, OR WOULD YOU ADVISE ME TO CALL AN ATTORNEY?"

8/20/89

"MY OLDEST WAS AN ALL-NATURAL DELIVERY.... THEN FREDDY WAS CAESAREAN .... JENNY WAS IN VITRO..... AND THE TWINS CAME FREEZE-DRIED IN THEIR OWN RESEALABLE ZIP-LOCK STORAGE BAGS."

2/25/94

JIM BORGMAN
CINCINNATI ENQUIRER ©1994
Mary is seventeen, unwed and pregnant.
What will the other kids say?
MOM'S HAVING ANOTHER BABY?!!

9/27/91

GOODNIGHT, DR. SEUSS

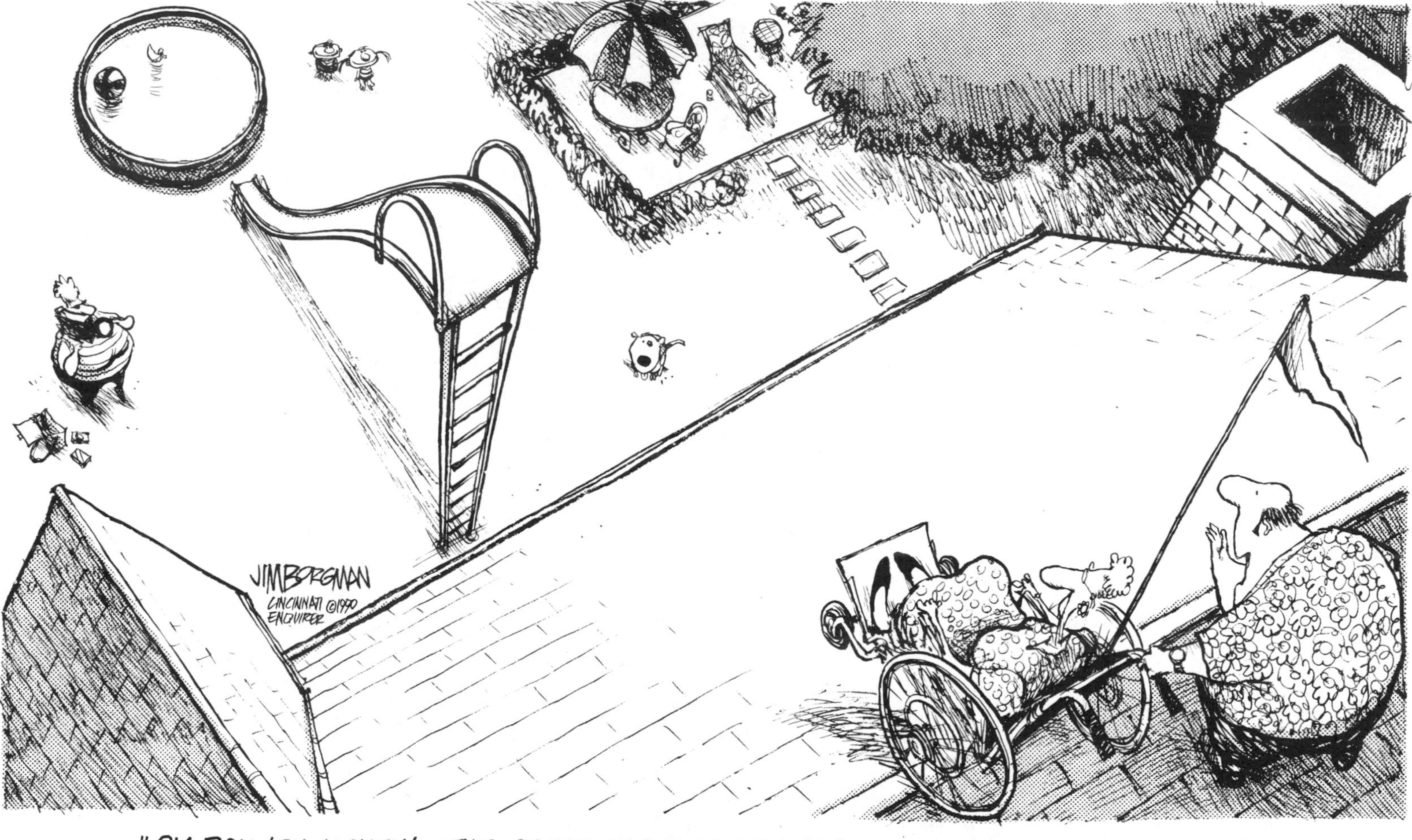

"OK, ROLL 'EM, HONEY! .... THIS OUGHT TO GET US ON 'AMERICA'S FUNNIEST HOME VIDEOS' FOR SURE!"

10/7/91

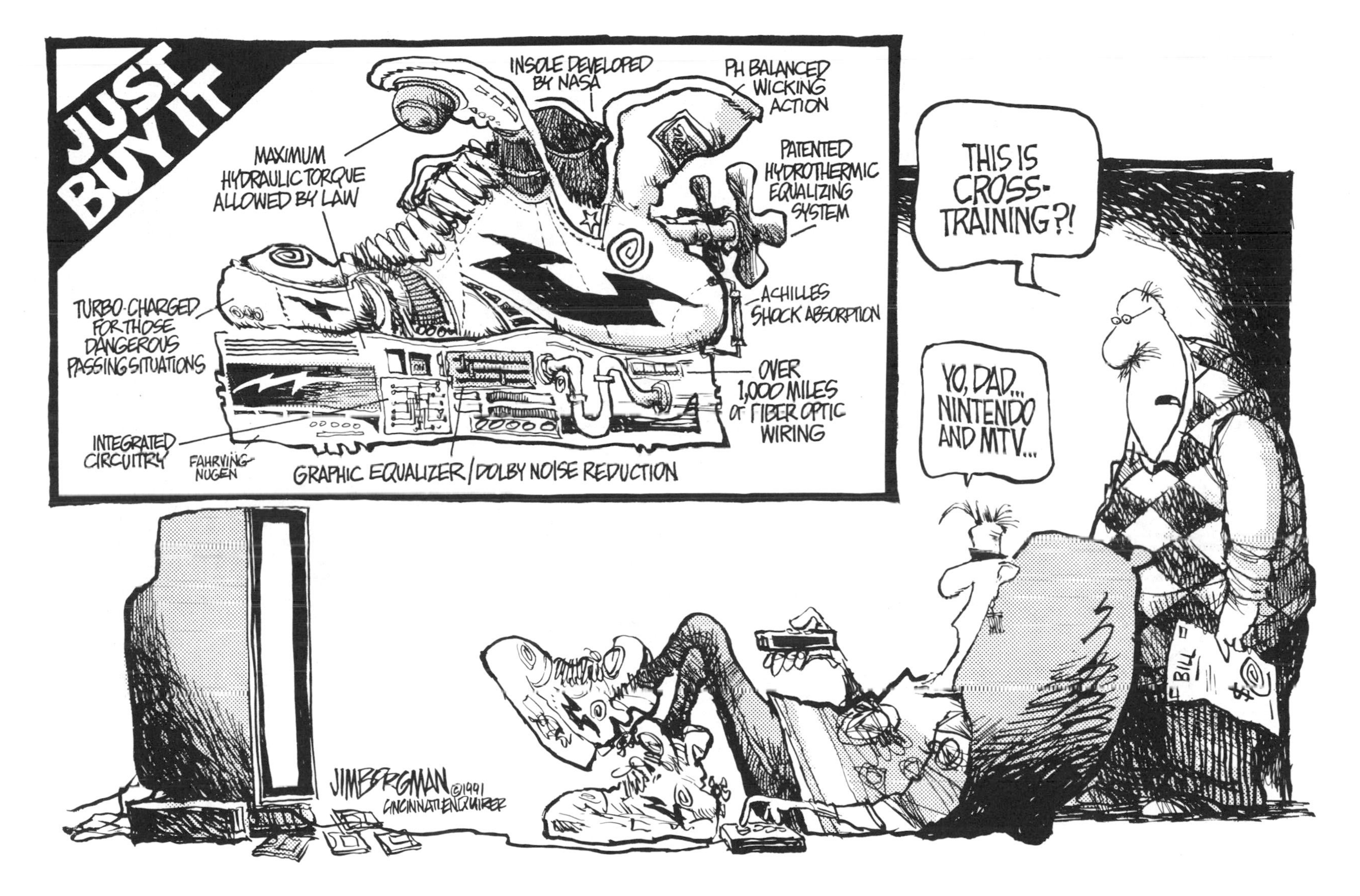

JUST BUY IT
INSOLE DEVELOPED BY NASA
PH BALANCED WICKING ACTION
MAXIMUM HYDRAULIC TORQUE ALLOWED BY LAW
PATENTED HYDROTHERMIC EQUALIZING SYSTEM
TURBO-CHARGED FOR THOSE DANGEROUS PASSING SITUATIONS
ACHILLES SHOCK ABSORPTION
OVER 1,000 MILES OF FIBER OPTIC WIRING
INTEGRATED CIRCUITRY
FAHRVING-NUGEN
GRAPHIC EQUALIZER/DOLBY NOISE REDUCTION
THIS IS CROSS-TRAINING?!
YO, DAD... NINTENDO AND MTV...
BILL
JIM BERGMAN ©1991 CINCINNATI ENQUIRER

4/22/91

GOOD MORNING, TEACHER

2/10/91

Downwardly adjusting ACADEMIC EXPECTATIONS for MAXIMAL ALIGNMENT with Existing PERFORMANCE Realities
JIM BORGMAN CINCINNATI ENQUIRER ©1991
OK, NOW TRY IT...
SCHOOLS

6/22/90

"SHE'S A MESS ALRIGHT.... YOUR CELLULAR PHONE JAMMED UP AND CAUSED YOUR ANSWERING MACHINE TO THROW A ROD.... THEN SHE OVERHEATED AND YOUR FAX MACHINE BLEW A GASKET."

6/13/95

"I KNEW WE WERE GETTING TELEPHONE SERVICE THROUGH OUR CABLE TV, AND TRANSMITTING DOCUMENTS THROUGH OUR COPIER, BUT WHEN DID WE START GETTING FAXES THROUGH OUR TOASTER OVEN?"

IT'S OVER
THIRD WORLD
GORBACHEV
ANY PORT IN A STORM
"LOOK, EVERYBODY! IT'S BORIS YELTSIN'S PREDECESSOR!"

The Pitter-Patter of Little Democracies

THE PITTER-PATTER OF LITTLE DEMOCRACIES

2/22/90

LEOPARD HAVING ITS SPOTS CHANGED

1/22/90

10/9/89

1/30/90

4/23/91

2/4/91

6/19/91

12/27/91

MIKHAIL GORBACHEV MONUMENT
LENIN
JIM BORGMAN
CINCINNATI ENQUIRER©1991

2/4/90

"NOW THAT COMMUNISM IS DEAD, I THINK I'LL TAKE A NAP."

10/1/91

"EASTERN EUROPE SUBDIVIDED AGAIN TODAY...."

9/30/91

ETHNICITY
COMMUNISM
TYRANNY
JIM BORGMAN
CINCINNATI ENQUIRER
©1991

9/12/91

"YOU'RE.... TAKING..... IT..... ALL?....."

12/18/90

JIMBORGMAN
CINCINNATI ENQUIRER©1990
COULD WE BORROW A CUP OF FLOUR?

8/6/91

WINNER AND LOSER

10/5/90

JIMBORGMAN
CINCINNATI
ENQUIRER©1990
REUNIFICATION
SOUTH
AFRICA
GERMANY

2/19/90

4/29/94

IT'S MORNING IN SOUTH AFRICA

1/6/93

ADDING TO THE ASHHEAP OF HISTORY

5/4/90

JIM BORGMAN
CINCINNATI ENQUIRER ©1990
NUCLEAR-WEAPONS PLANTS
RHETORIC

2/27/94

I COULD HAVE DIED A HERO.
HERO
JIM BORGMAN CINCINNATI ENQUIRER ©1994
MISSILES CUBA
MY COUNTRY WAS AT WAR, A COLD WAR. WE THOUGHT THE BOMBS COULD DROP ANY TIME.
NO ONE KNEW WHAT WOULD HAPPEN IF THEY DID. THEY NEEDED TESTS.
CANCER
MY DAYS WERE NUMBERED.
RADIATION LAB
IF YOU'D HAVE ASKED I WOULD HAVE VOLUNTEERED. OTHERS WOULD HAVE, TOO. FOR OUR KIDS.
BUT YOU NEVER ASKED.
I COULD HAVE DIED A HERO.
VICTIM

"NO, I MEANT I REALLY, REALLY, REALLY, REALLY, REALLY NEED YOUR HELP..."
CLIFF'S NOTES
QUAYLE
deer caught in the headlights
READ THESE BABIES
READ 'EM AND WEEP.
OFFICE OF THE VICE PRESIDENT
PENCILS
"WHAT NOW, MR. PRESIDENT? EVERY PENCIL IN THE WHITE HOUSE IS

Flashback

AN EAR TO THE GROUND

11/17/88

COME ON, DANNY.... WE'RE GOING TO THE WHITE HOUSE!
WOW! LET'S GO GET 'EM!
TRANSITION OR BURST!
COMIX
JIMBORGMAN
CINCINNATI ENQUIRER©1988

1/12/89

JIM BORGMAN
The CINCINNATI ENQUIRER ©1989
INAUGURATION DAY 1989
HOLY BIBLE
CLIFF'S NOTES
PRESIDENT BUSH
VICE-PRESIDENT QUAYLE

8/12/90

TIMEOUT FOR RELOADING

5/20/90

* MAY NOT INCLUDE LICENSE, TITLE, DEALER PREP, WHITEWALLS, OPTION PACKAGES, ACCESSORIES, RUSTPROOFING, DEALER OR MANUFACTURER'S WARRANTEE, REBATES, CHROME, INTERIOR, TRANSMISSION, AERIALS, STEREO OR AIR CONDITIONING. YOUR MILEAGE MAY VARY. OFFER NOT AVAILABLE IN AK, AL, AZ, CA, CT, FL, GA, HI, KY, LA, MA, ME, MI, MO, MS, MT, NC, ND, NH, NY, OH, OK, PA, RI, SC, SD, TX, UT, VT, WA, WV, WY, DISTRICT OF COLUMBIA AND PUERTO RICO. CHECK LOCAL LISTINGS FOR SCHEDULING IN YOUR AREA. INDIVIDUAL RESTRICTIONS MAY APPLY. NO ONE UNDER 18 ADMITTED WITHOUT PARENT OR LEGAL GUARDIAN. THE SURGEON GENERAL HAS DETERMINED THAT CURRENT TAX RATES ARE HAZARDOUS TO FEDERAL BUDGETING. DO NOT ATTEMPT THIS AT HOME. IF INGESTED INDUCE VOMITING. PRODUCT MAY CONTAIN ONE OR MORE OF THE FOLLOWING INGREDIENTS: PALM OIL, COCONUT OIL, SNAKE OIL. CONTENTS MAY SETTLE DURING SHIPMENT. SOLD BY WEIGHT, NOT BY VOLUME. ANY ACCOUNTS, DESCRIPTIONS OR REBROADCASTS OF THIS TRANSMISSION WITHOUT THE EXPRESSED, WRITTEN CONSENT OF MAJOR LEAGUE BASEBALL ARE STRICTLY PROHIBITED. USUAL RESTRICTIONS APPLY. OFFER VOID TO EMPLOYEES AND IMMEDIATE FAMILIES. ALL RIGHTS RESERVED. NOT INTENDED AS A SUBSTITUTE FOR PARENTAL SUPERVISION. VOID WHERE PROHIBITED. LICENSED DRIVERS ONLY. IF PAIN PERSISTS CONTACT YOUR PHYSICIAN. PAYMENTS BASED ON 48 MOS. AT 11.75% APR VARIABLE WITH APPROVED CREDIT. 'READ MY LIPS' IS A REGISTERED TRADEMARK OF THE 'GEORGE BUSH FOR PRESIDENT' CAMPAIGN COMMITTEE AND IS NOT INTENDED AS LEGALLY OR ETHICALLY BINDING. FOR A COMPLETE LIST OF CAVEAT'S FINE PRINT CONTACT: RICHARD DARMAN, OFFICE OF DUCK TESTS, QUACK QUACK, QUACK AVE NW, WASHINGTON, DC 20500. PATENT PENDING.

4/9/89

JIM BORGMAN CINCINNATI ENQUIRER ©1989
EXXON VALDEZ
BY GAWD, SOMEBODY'S GOING TO PAY FOR THIS!!
DING DING DING DING DING DING DING DING
1.79
USA

5/4/89

OIL INDUSTRY
SLICKS HAPPEN
JIMBORGMAN
CINCINNATI ENQUIRER ©1989

8/2/89

CLEANUP PHASE II

6/27/90

WHO? WHO? WHO? WHO? WHO?
OLD-GROWTH FORESTS
MAN
JIM BORGMAN
CINCINNATI ©1990 ENQUIRER

7/24/90

"AS A MATTER OF FACT, I'D LIKE TO SEE SOME IDENTIFICATION FROM YOU, TOO."

11/5/91

"INTERESTING.... IN THIS SHRED HE ACCUSES THE PRESIDENT OF A MASSIVE COVER-UP...."

5/1/92

LIAR!
JIM BORGMAN
CINCINNATI ENQUIRER ©1992
EXHIBIT A
RODNEY KING CASE

5/5/92

5/7/92

A QUIZ for WHITE AMERICANS:
Q: IF THIS IS HOW YOUR COUNTRY PORTRAYED ITSELF, HOW MUCH A PART OF IT DO YOU THINK YOU'D FEEL?
JUSTI
THE PRESIDENT
JIM BORGMAN CINCINNATI ENQUIRER ©1992

5/3/92

JIMBORGMAN
HOW CAN WE BE SURE SHE'S AWAKE?...
ACQUITTAL OUTRAGES AMERICA
DOUBLE STANDARD OF JUSTICE?

4/30/92

"BUT...BUT.....WE HAVE A STANDARD OF LIVING TO MAINTAIN AROUND HERE.....!"

6/4/92

"OH, I GIVE UP! NOW HE'S NOT EVEN TAKING NOTES!..."

6/10/90

CONSUME!
THROW AWAY THAT OLD ONE
YOU NEED A NEW ONE!
Run Right Out and BUY ONE!
BUY MORE STUFF
KEEP GETTING MORE
USE IT AN THROW IT AWA
CONSUME More!
KEEP ACQUIRING MORE
DISPOSA
DISPOSE and BUY MORE
REPLACE THAT OLD ONE WITH This Year's Model!
CONSUME
BUY MORE! MORE! MORE!
* SIGH *
RECYCLE
JIM BORGMAN CINCINNATI ENQUIRER ©1990

10/13/89

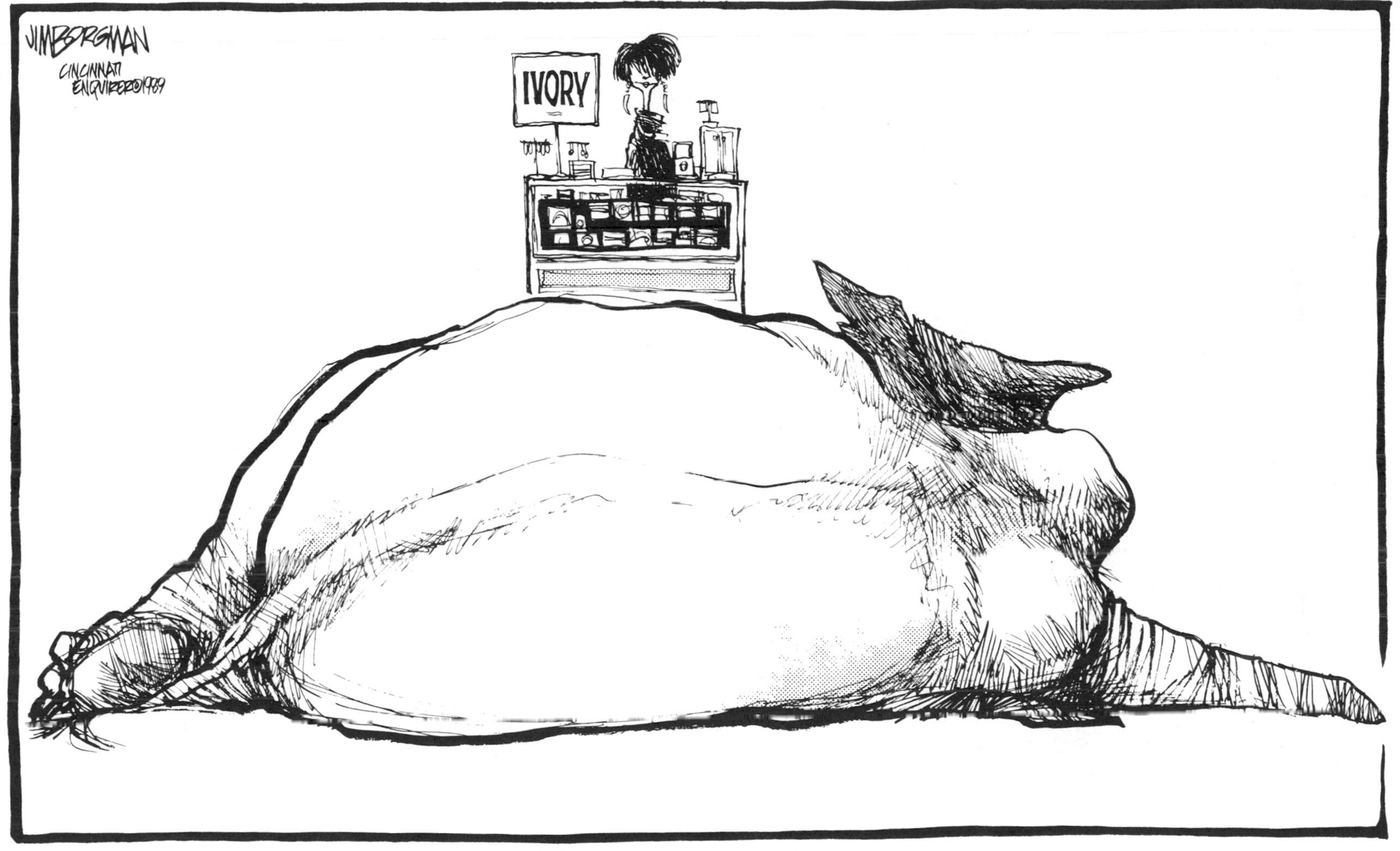

ELEPHANT GRAVEYARD

"SORRY... I'M SUFFERING FROM COMPASSION FATIGUE."

10/18/90

JIMBORGMAN
CINCINNATI ENQUIRER ©1990
CALM....
PRUDENT....
NOT RATTLED....
IM-PER-TURBABLE...
DING
DING
DING
DING
DING
DING
DING
CRISES

CLICK
CLICK
CLICK
SADDAM
"DAMN, THERE GOES THE CABLE AGAIN!"
PULLING ALL SADDAM'S TEETH
"WHAT DO YOU
THE AWARDING of the IRAQI
Order of Hammurabi
WILL THE LAST ONE OUT OF IRAQ

Saddam and Gomorrah

1/15/91

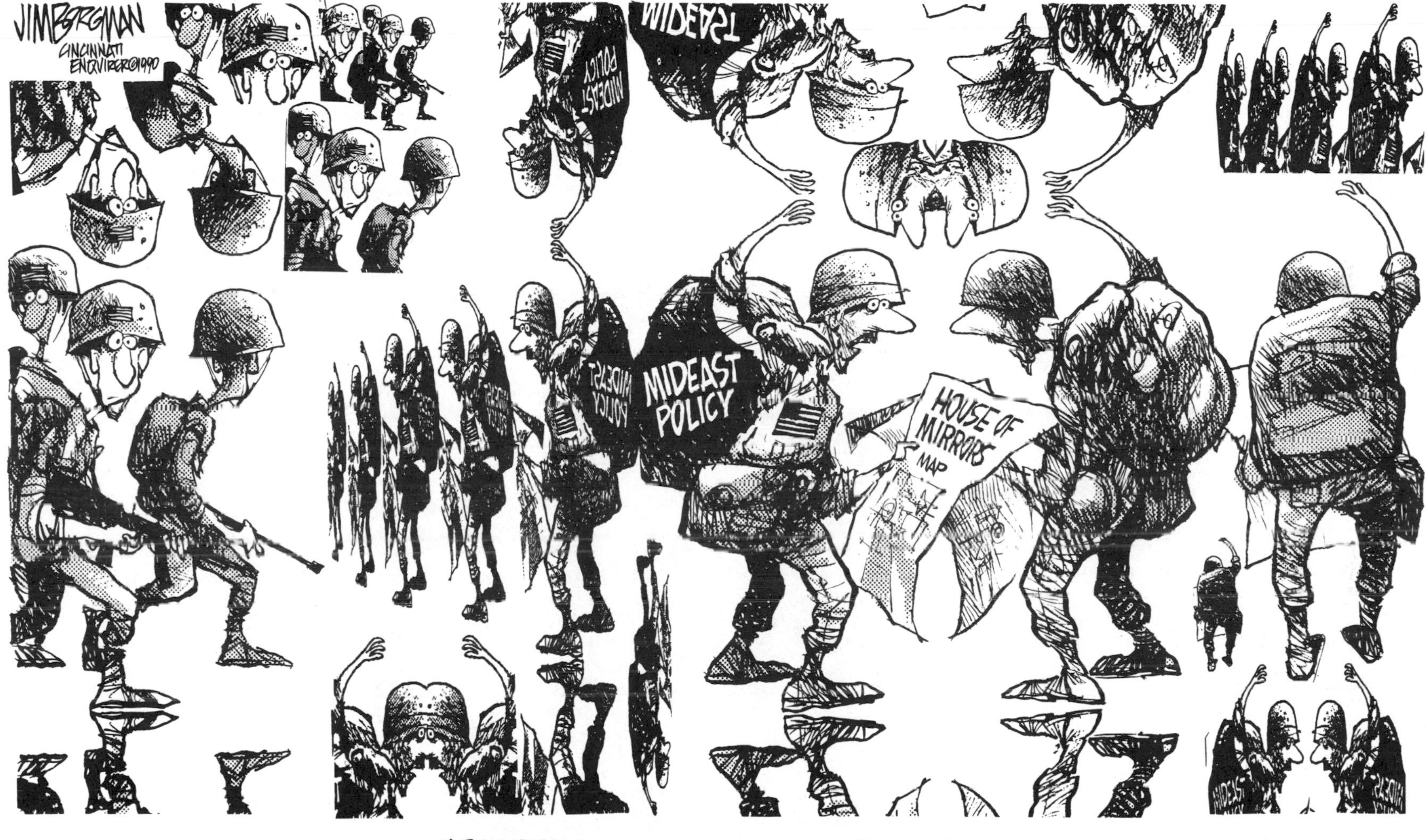

"FOLLOW ME...THIS WAY.....I THINK......"

2/28/91

JIM BORGMAN
CINCINNATI ENQUIRER ©1991
NOBEL PEACE PRIZE
1990
1991
NOBEL APPEASEMENT PRIZE

A THOUSAND POINTS OF LIGHT

2/13/91

GROUND WAR

2/3/91

"WELL, TOM, WE'VE DONE IT AGAIN.... WE'VE REDUCED THE WAR IN THE GULF TO ANOTHER NEATLY-PACKAGED MEDIA EVENT WITH ITS OWN COMPUTER-ANIMATED LOGO, THEME OF THE DAY, STUDIO ANALYSTS, SOUND BITES AND DEMONSTRATIONS ON CUE... BUT WAR IS NOT A SUPER BOWL, TOM.... which is 'Commentary' for today... NOW, BACK UP TO THE BOOTH."

2/22/91

JIM BORGMAN
CINCINNATI ENQUIRER ©1991
The Much-Vaunted!!!
IRAQI
WAR MACHINE
CALL the CRACK SPARE PARTS DIVISION AND ORDER ANOTHER DOZEN state-of-the-art WIRE COAT HANGERS...
The Elite IRAQI GREASEMONKEY Corps

2/27/91

The MOTHER OF ALL BATTLES
IRAQ
MOMMY!!
KUWAIT
JIMBORGMAN
CINCINNATI ENQUIRER©1991

3/5/91

JIM BORGMAN
CINCINNATI ENQUIRER ©1991
The Strategists
XVIII CORPS
SCHWARZKOPF
DUMMKOPF
40 DIVISIONS
X INTERVIEW WITH WOLF BLITZER
SURRENDER TO ITALIAN CAMERA CREW
X SURRENDER TO PEEWEE HERMAN
THROW GRENADE
X EPW CAMP
MOM'S DINER
PULL PIN X
FOR IRS USE ONLY
LEFT FOOT IN
LEFT FOOT OUT
X HOKEY POKEY
TIC TAC

4/9/91

"PARTY POOPER!"

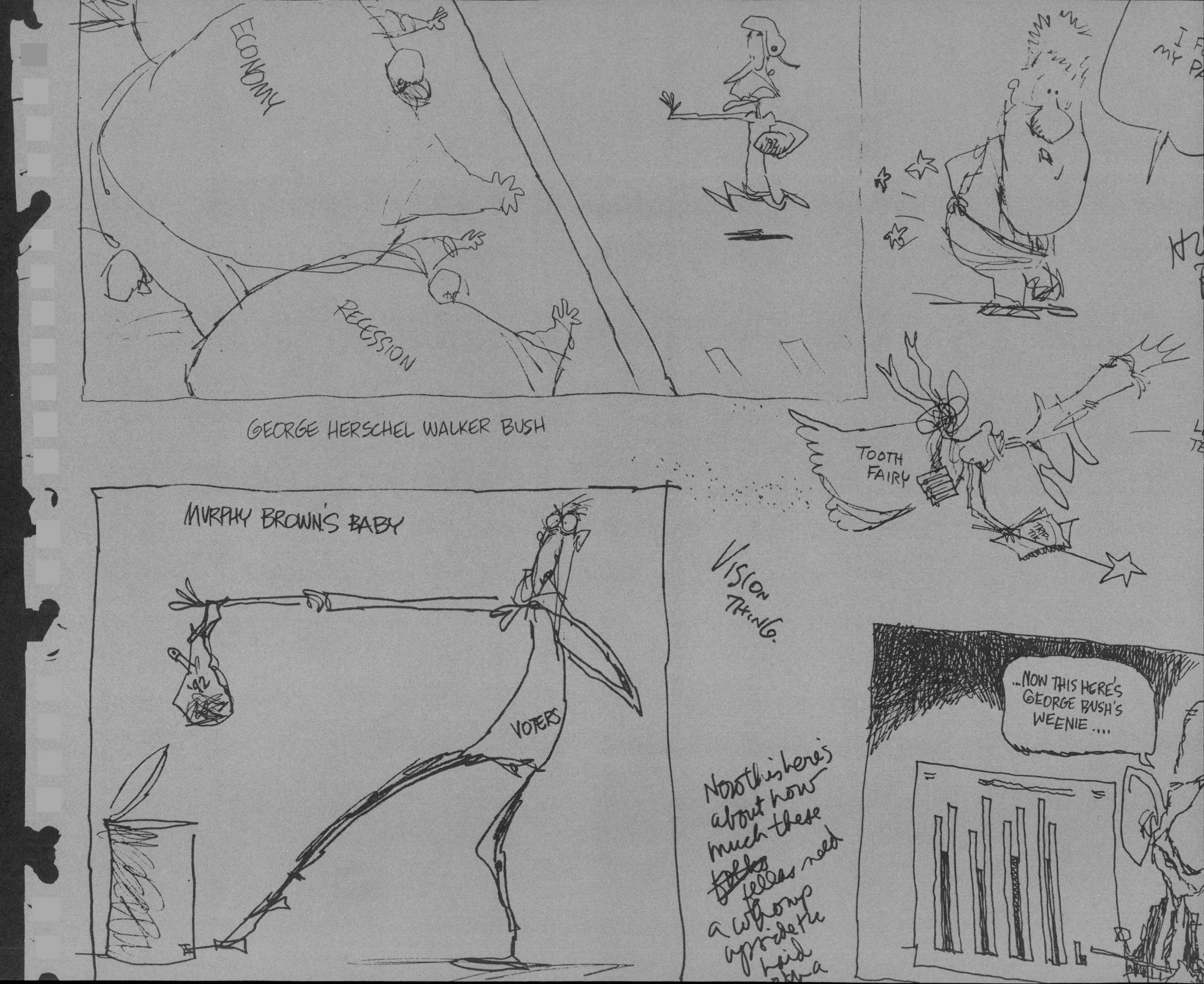
ECONOMY
RECESSION
GEORGE HERSCHEL WALKER BUSH
TOOTH FAIRY
MURPHY BROWN'S BABY
'92
VOTERS
VISION THING.
...NOW THIS HERE'S GEORGE BUSH'S WEENIE....
Now this here's about how much these folks fellas need a whomp upside the haid

The Bill Comes Due

THE BILL COMES DUE

9/20/92

GEORGE HERSCHEL WALKER BUSH

MY
THIS AND THAT and A BIT OF THIS OTHER THING, JUST A TOUCH OF SOMETHING ELSE, A SPLASH OF ADJUSTMENT ON ONE THING and ANOTHER, HOLD THE COURSE
A LITTLE SPRINKLING OF THIS AND THAT, MAYBE TRY AN IDEA OR TWO, WHAT THE HECK
THEN WE'LL TRY A BIT OF THIS AND SOMETHING ELSE, VERY PRUDENT, NOT GUNNA DO ANYTHING DRASTIC, NO SIR, GUNNA FIGURE IT OUT AND GO DO IT
ADD A SMIDGEON OF WHATCHAMACALLIT AND LET ME JUST ADD, WE'RE NOT TALKING SOME CRAZY HALF-BAKED PROPOSALS, GONNA THINK IT THROUGH, FORM A TASK FORCE, CONSIDER ALL THE REPERCUSSIONS, RUN IT UP THE FLAGPOLE, TAKE A LOOK AT THE POLLS, CHECK IT OUT.
A TOUCH OF THIS THING OVER HERE, THEN STEP BACK and SEE WHAT WE WANNA DO NEXT. TRY A SPLASH OF SOMETHING, ADJUST FOR IT, BACK OFF IF IT GETS TOO HOT, BE PRUDENT
ITEM VETO PROPOSAL, THEN WE'RE GONNA BLAME CONGRESS AND HAUL OUT THE OLD LINE-
MISCELLANEOUS JAZZ, ASK FOR A BALANCED BUDGET AMENDMENT AGAIN THEN SOME
THIS AND THAT AND THIS AND THAT AND THIS AND THAT AND THIS AND THAT AND THIS AND THAT AND THIS AND THAT AND THIS AND THAT
THIS AND THAT AND MORE OF SAME BECAUSE HEY, IT'S WORKING
SO AGAIN, WE DON'T WANT TO DO ANYTHING RASH, JUST BASH THE DEMOCRATS,
NOTHING YOU HAVEN'T EVER HEARD BEFORE, MORE OF SAME, AND ALL THAT
THROW A FEW VAGUE SUGGESTIONS OUT THERE, BLAME ALL THE USUAL VILLAINS: LAWYERS, THE PRESS, CONGRESS, HOLLYWOOD
THE CULTURAL ELITE, BLAH BLAH ESPECIALLY CONGRESS
JUST KEEP GIVING ME MORE TIME, THE BLAME GAME, SO IN CONCLUSION, YOU KNOW, THE SAME OLD STUFF
JIM BORGMAN in HOUSTON '92

4/29/92

JIM BORGMAN
CINCINNATI ENQUIRER ©1992
JUST
TAKE A POLL, CONSULT THE BIG CONTRIBUTORS,
APPOINT A COMMITTEE, PLOT A FALLBACK POSITION,
BUILD IN AN ESCAPE HATCH, SEND UP A TRIAL BALLOON AND
DO
IT.
CONGRESS

3/22/92

CHECK BOUNCING LATEST OUTRAGE
FLICK
VOTERS!
CONGRESS
JIM BORGMAN
CINCINNATI ENQUIRER ©1992

3/23/92

JIM BORGMAN CINCINNATI ENQUIRER ©1992
NATIONAL AGENDA
BUSH '92
BUSH '92
STARCH
BUSH '92

2/19/92

JIM BORGMAN CINCINNATI ENQUIRER ©1992

MURPHY BROWN'S BABY

7/28/92

MEMO
You can't fir me.
I quite.
—Dan
JIM BORGMAN CINCINNATI ENQUIRER ©1992

10/20/92

" IT REALLY BUGS ME THAT CLINTON WAS OVER IN ENGLAND PROTESTING THE VIETNAM WAR....
HECK, WE NEEDED HIM HERE AT HOME PROTESTING THE VIETNAM WAR!"

JIM BORGMAN
CINCINNATI ENQUIRER
©1992
HE'S STILL BREATHING... LOOKS LIKE HE'S OUR NOMINEE.
DEMS
CLINTON

10/9/92

JIM BORGMAN CINCINNATI ENQUIRER ©1992
THE LAST TWELVE PEA-BRAINED GODFSAKEN BLACK-EYED FLEA-BITTEN YEARS, AS IF I AIN'T BEEN SAYIN' SO FOR LORD KNOWS HOW LONG
1980 1981 1982 1983 1984 1985 1986 1987 1988 1989 1990 1991 1992
...NOW THIS HERE'S ABOUT HOW MUCH THESE FELLAS NEED A GOOD WHOMP UPSIDE THE HEAD WITH A FIVE HUNNERD DOLLAR HAMMER.

11/4/92

BLOW, BIG MAN, BLOW

CLINTON
GORE 92
Daughter to Work Day
PUT IT ALL IN PORK BELLIES.
HILLARY, I'M GONNA BE A LITTLE LATE TONIGHT...
Aspin Blvd.
BILL
OH,
"I SEE WHAT HE'S UP TO! DOING! HE'S PACKING THE COURT WITH A BUNCH OF MODERATES!"
Breyer
ALASKA
CALL THE NATIO
ARCHIVES
WE'VE GOT TO FIND THAT RECEIPT.
Bobby Ray
Inman
ZHIRINOVSKY WANTS

Don't Stop Thinking About Tomorrow

"OK, EVERYBODY INHALE...."

7/22/92

BR
ONK
Clinton-Gore BUS TOUR '92
JIMBORGMAN
CINCINNATI ENQUIRER ©1992

11/9/92

JIMBORGMAN
CINCINNATI ENQUIRER©1992
FIRST 100 DAYS
ROSS
JOBS!
SCHOOLS!
HEALTH CARE!
WELFARE REFORM!
DEFICIT REDUCTION!
BANKS!
CAPITAL GAINS CUT!
ENVIRONMENT!
FAMILY LEAVE!
DRUGS!
CAMPAIGN REFORM!
FOREIGN TRADE!
HEADSTART!
EDUCATION!
CITIES!
STUDENT LOANS!
HOUSING!
HOMELESS!
CIVIL RIGHTS!
"HERE Y'GO, SON.....YOU'RE GONNA NEED THESE BAD BOYS MORE'N I DO."

1/15/93

"OK, BILL, I SEE YOU'VE MET THAT CRAZY AUNT I WAS TELLING YOU ABOUT..... WELL, HERE'S THE DEAL: SHE'S ALL YOURS."

1/21/93

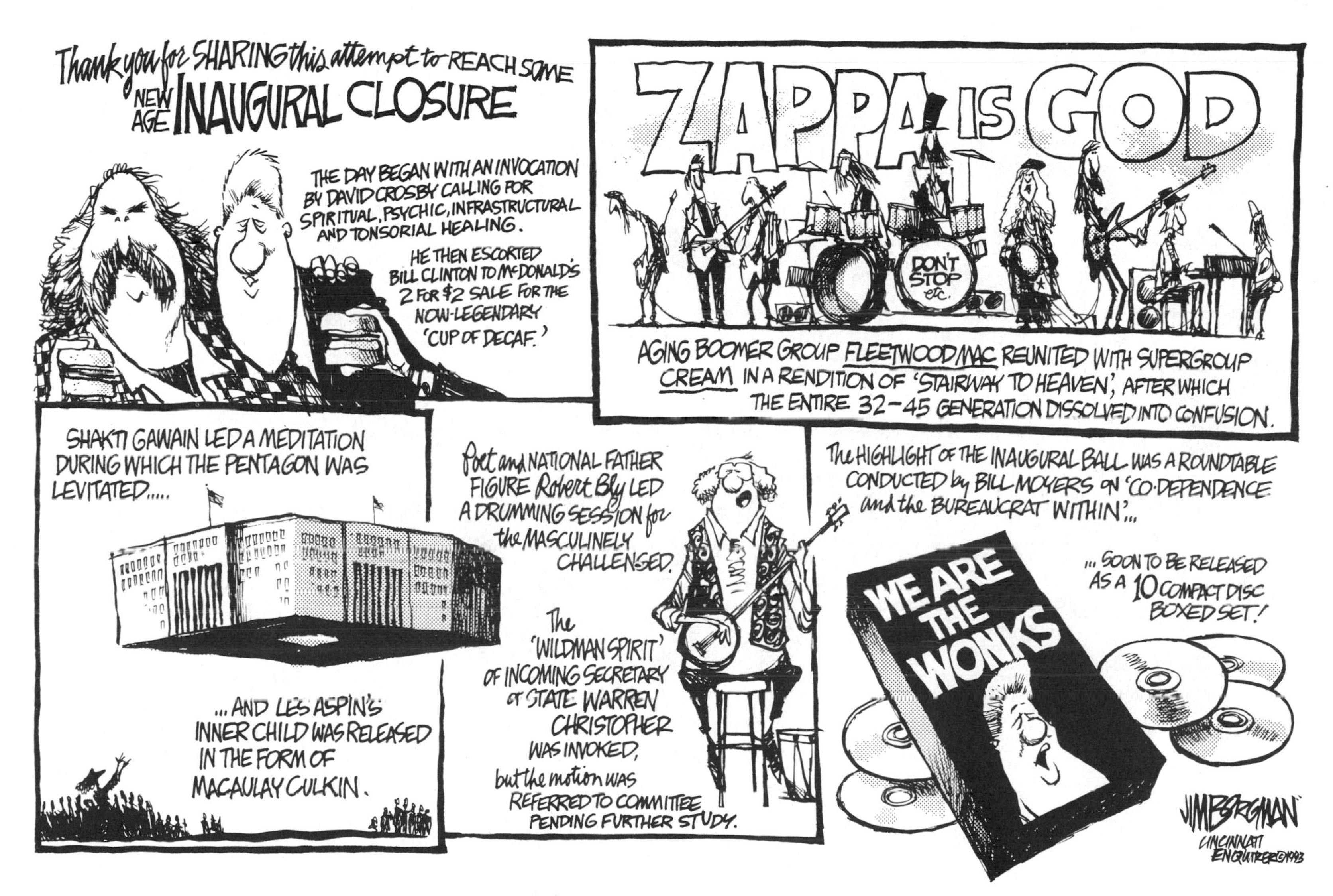

Thank you for SHARING this attempt to REACH SOME NEW AGE INAUGURAL CLOSURE
THE DAY BEGAN WITH AN INVOCATION BY DAVID CROSBY CALLING FOR SPIRITUAL, PSYCHIC, INFRASTRUCTURAL AND TONSORIAL HEALING.
HE THEN ESCORTED BILL CLINTON TO McDONALD'S 2 FOR $2 SALE FOR THE NOW-LEGENDARY 'CUP OF DECAF.'
ZAPPA IS GOD
DON'T STOP etc.
AGING BOOMER GROUP FLEETWOOD MAC REUNITED WITH SUPERGROUP CREAM IN A RENDITION OF 'STAIRWAY TO HEAVEN,' AFTER WHICH THE ENTIRE 32-45 GENERATION DISSOLVED INTO CONFUSION.
SHAKTI GAWAIN LED A MEDITATION DURING WHICH THE PENTAGON WAS LEVITATED.....
...AND LES ASPIN'S INNER CHILD WAS RELEASED IN THE FORM OF MACAULAY CULKIN.
Poet and NATIONAL FATHER FIGURE Robert Bly LED A DRUMMING SESSION for the MASCULINELY CHALLENGED.
The 'WILDMAN SPIRIT' OF INCOMING SECRETARY of STATE WARREN CHRISTOPHER WAS INVOKED, but the motion was REFERRED TO COMMITTEE PENDING FURTHER STUDY.
The HIGHLIGHT OF THE INAUGURAL BALL WAS A ROUNDTABLE CONDUCTED by BILL MOYERS ON 'CO-DEPENDENCE and the BUREAUCRAT WITHIN'...
WE ARE THE WONKS
...SOON TO BE RELEASED AS A 10 COMPACT DISC BOXED SET!
JIM BORGMAN
CINCINNATI ENQUIRER ©1993

1/11/93

"BESIDES THAT, CHELSEA, HOW DO YOU LIKE WASHINGTON?"

11/22/92

1/26/93

DAY
1
An inauspicious beginning...
JIM BORGMAN
CINCINNATI ENQUIRER ©1993
HONEYMOON SUITE
JUST MARRIED
ZOE BAIRD NOMIN

12/8/92

2/5/93

THE PRESIDENT CONTINUES TO DEMONSTRATE HIS UNCANNY KNACK FOR CROWD-PLEASING PROPOSALS.....

1/28/93

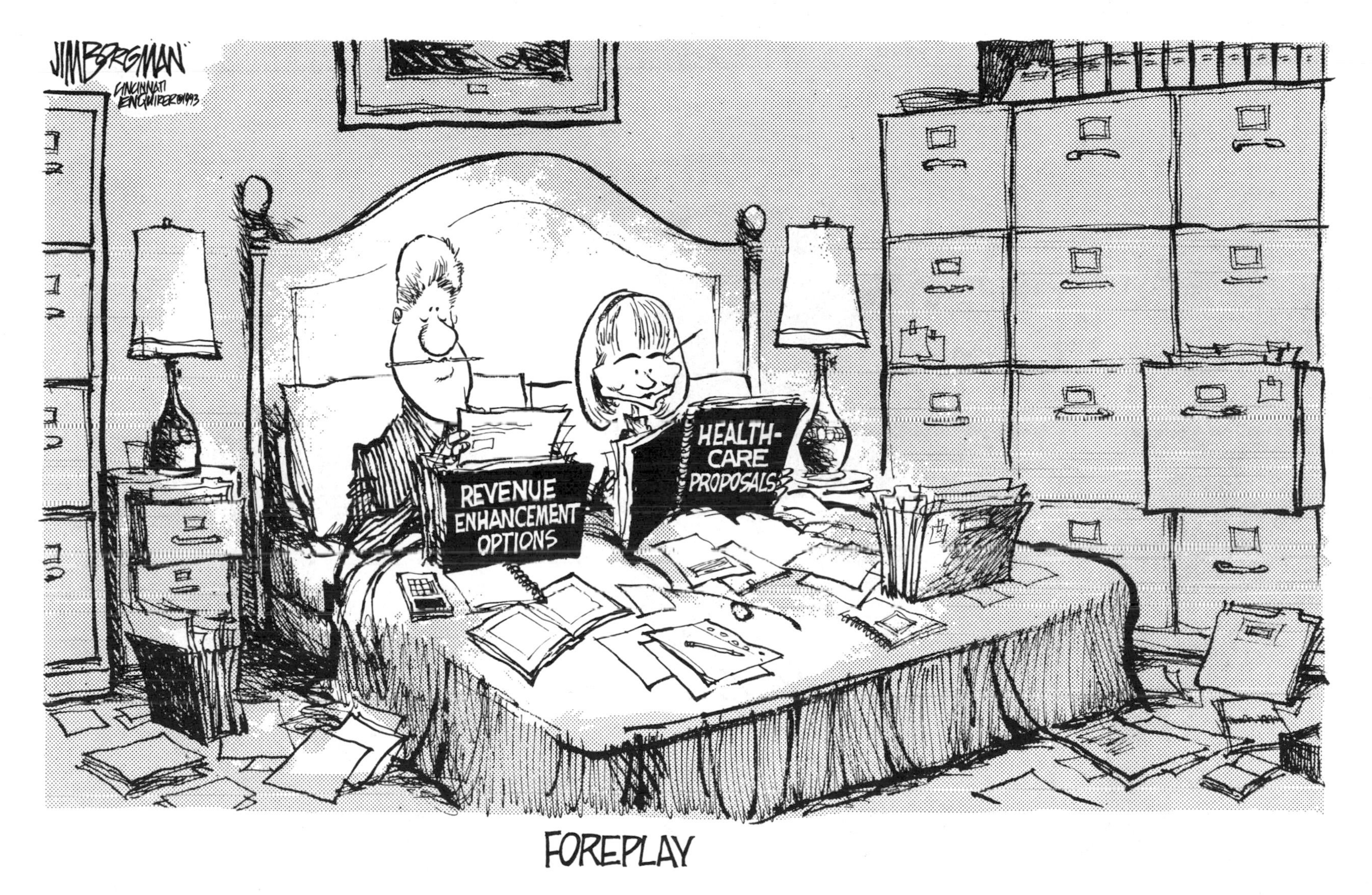

FOREPLAY

2/8/93

SOCIAL SECURITY
SHARED SACRIFICE
Don't Stop Thinking About Tomorrow.
JIM BORGMAN
CINCINNATI ENQUIRER©1993

4/19/94

JIM BORGMAN
CINCINNATI ENQUIRER ©1994
'Take Our Daughters to Work' Day
PUT IT ALL IN PORK BELLIES...
HILLARY

1/27/93

"HE WANTS TO KNOW, 'CAN YOU GET USED TO WRITING THE MAJORITY OPINION?'..."

7/22/94

"OH, I SEE WHAT HE'S UP TO! HE'S PACKING THE COURT WITH A BUNCH OF MODERATES!!"

1/23/94

JIM BORGMAN
CINCINNATI ENQUIRER ©1994
HILLARY, I'M GONNA BE A LITTLE LATE AGAIN TONIGHT...
BILL
Aspin Freeway
Zoe
Lani Guinier
Bobby Ray Inman Blvd.

8/2/94

"IT'S A SLOW RECOVERY, BUT IT IS A RECOVERY...."

7/5/94

NON-SELECTIVE SQUEEZING

12/10/92

1/12/94

"HOW COME I DON'T NEVER GET INVITED NOWHERE?!"

12/23/93

HELLO, NATIONAL ARCHIVES? WE'VE GOT TO FIND THAT RECEIPT...
ALASKA
ARCTIC CIRCLE
BARROW
KOTZEBUE
FAIRBANKS
JUNEAU
SITKA
KODIAK
SEWARD'S FOLLY
ZHIRINOVSKY WANTS ALASKA BACK
EXCUSE ME?
JIM BORGMAN
CINCINNATI ENQUIRER ©1993

NASA
HUBBLE RESCUE MISSION
NASA
"DANG! NOW THERE'S AN EYELASH ON IT!"
JUST TWEEZ
"NO, THE NAIL CLIPPERS MEGASTORE IS TWO MALLS
WARHOL TIME
15
"EVERYBODY GETS 15 MINUTES."
"Has anybody got the time.. this must have stopped."
MADONNA
"GEORGE FOREMAN IS A REAL HERO FOR US OLD GUYS.... ESPECIALLY IN THE SENSE OF WISHING WE COULD PUNCH OUT ALL THE YOUNG GUYS IN OUR LIFE."

I Hear America Singing

"SOMEBODY CHECK THE BATTERY IN THAT CLOCK.... SURELY WE'VE BEEN HERE FOR HOURS...!"

5/8/89

HERE WE GO AGAIN, AROUND AND AROUND AND AROUND...
ABORTION
TWO SIDES, NO MIDDLE GROUND... DOUBT, CONFUSION, MERCY, UNDERSTANDING — ALL ARE UNACCEPTABLE.
NO ROOM FOR AFFIRMING LIFE WITHOUT BEING DOGMATIC... NO ROOM FOR COMPASSION WITHOUT BEING MILITANT...
SEEMS TO ME EVERYBODY HAS RIGHTS IN THIS, BUT NOBODY HAS ALL THE RIGHTS.
JIM BORGMAN
CINCINNATI ENQUIRER ©1989
THE TRUTH IS, I'M PRO-LIFE AND PRO-CHOICE.

4/27/92

JIM BORGMAN
CINCINNATI ENQUIRER ©1992
GOOD PEOPLE CAN DISAGREE ON ABORTION.
BABBLE-KILLER!!
WHAT IF JESUS WAS ABORTED
IF ABORTION IS OUTLAWE ONLY OUTLA
IT'S MY BODY, SO YOU SHOULD PAY FOR MY ABOR
CLINIC
THANK YOUR DOCTOR FOR NOT ABORTING YOU
LIFE IS PRECIOUS ...UNTIL BIRTH
PRO-CHO
THANK YOU FOR NO SMOKING
RESPONSIBI -NOT!
LIFE BE
IT'S A PROB, NOT A CHOIC

5/5/87

11/9/91

"WE NEED MORE THAN MAGIC ..... WE NEED MIRACLES."

4/10/90

A PLACE WHERE NO ONE IS AFRAID TO HUG

4/14/94

Generation X at a Y in the Road

5/9/90

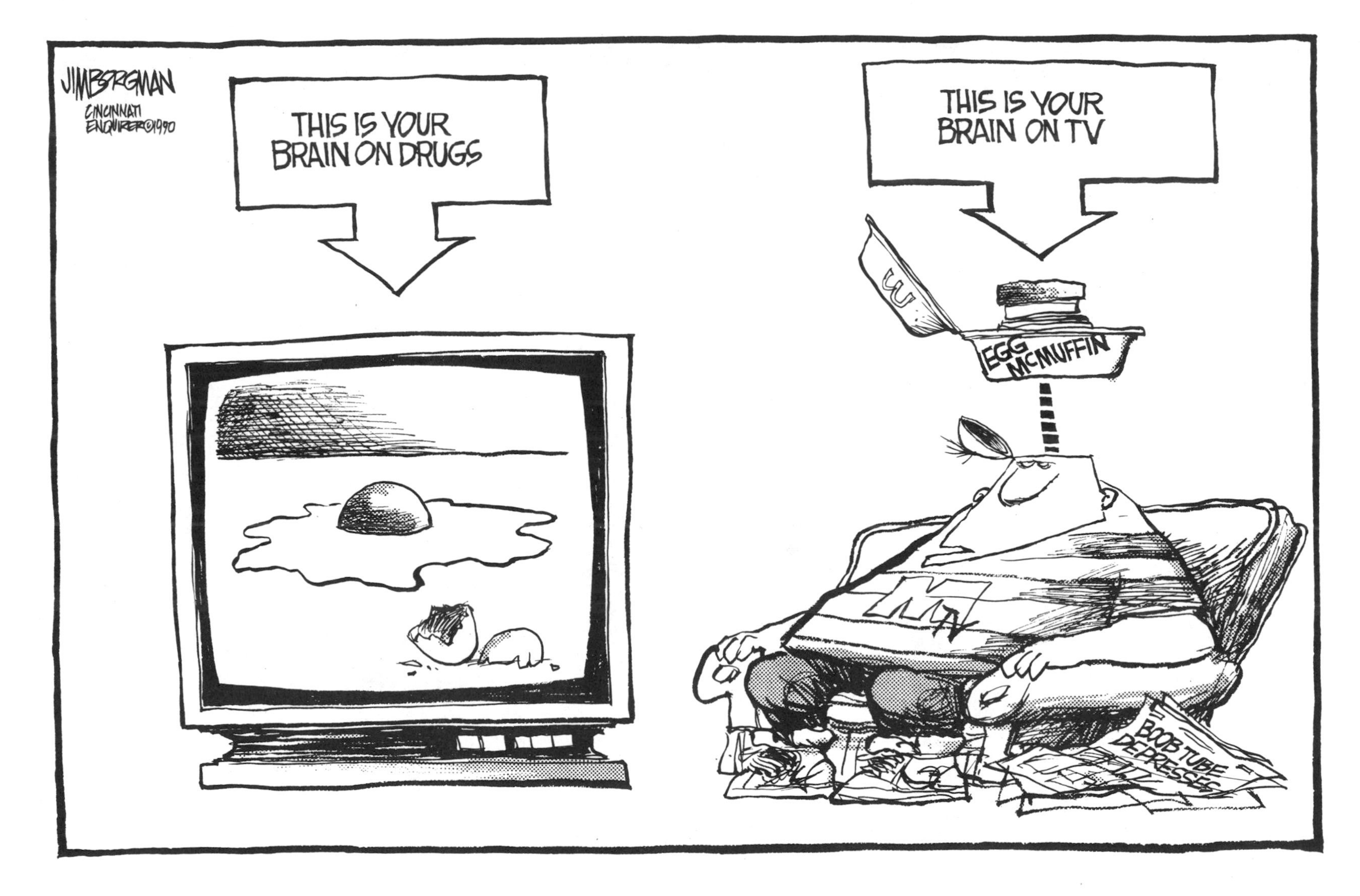
JIMBORGMAN
CINCINNATI
ENQUIRER©1990
THIS IS YOUR
BRAIN ON DRUGS
THIS IS YOUR
BRAIN ON TV
EGG
McMUFFIN
BOOB TUBE
DEPRESSES

5/29/94

JIM BORGMAN
CINCINNATI ENQUIRER ©1994
WHICH PART DON'T YOU UNDERSTAND?
GUNS KILL

4/26/94

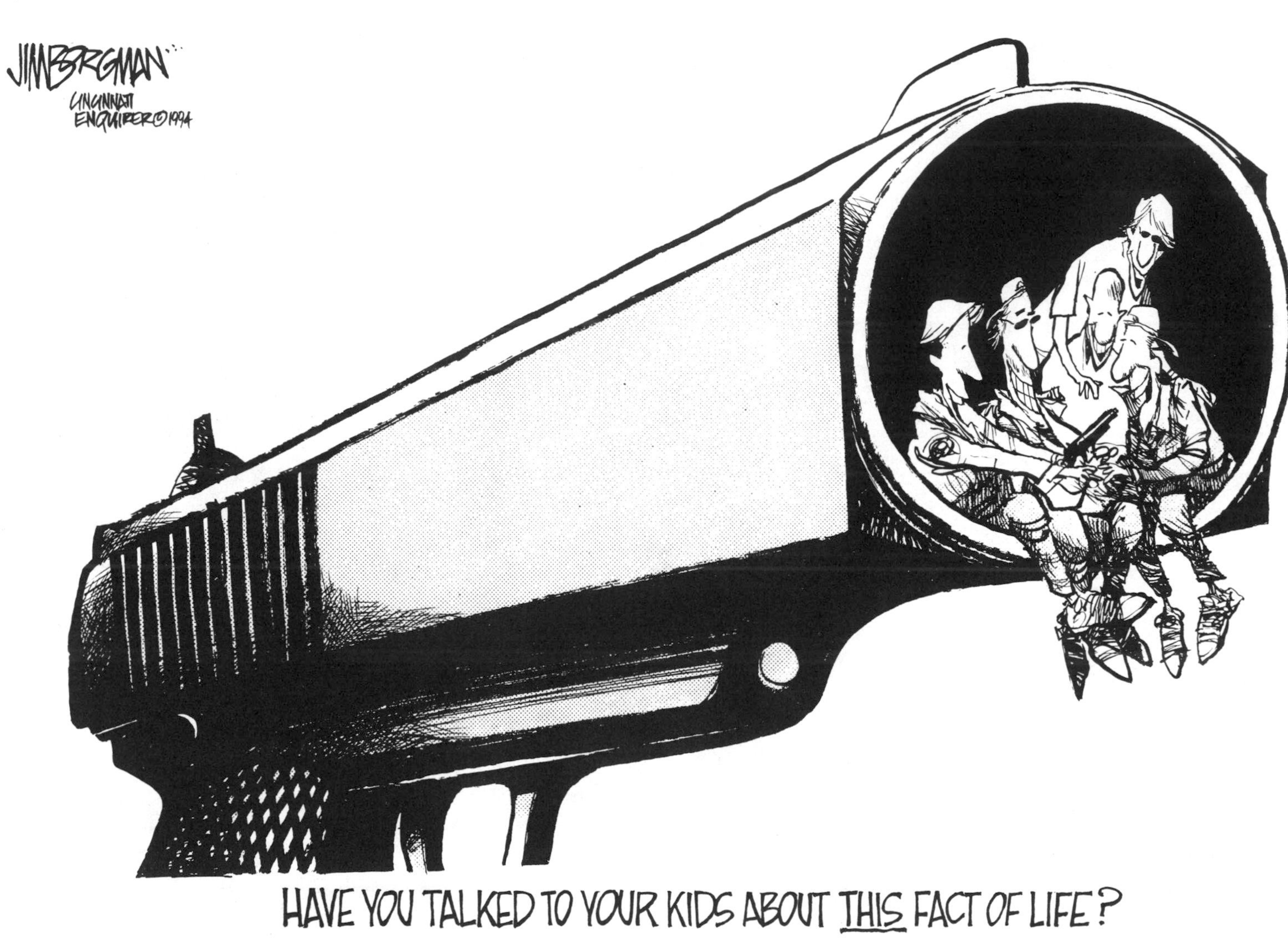
JIMBORGMAN
CINCINNATI ENQUIRER ©1994
HAVE YOU TALKED TO YOUR KIDS ABOUT THIS FACT OF LIFE?

5/12/95

JIMBORGMAN
CINCINNATI ENQUIRER ©1995
GUNS DON'T KILL CHILDREN. CHILDREN KILL CHILDREN.
NRA

7/6/88

THE SPIKE IS DRIVEN CONNECTING ALL THE MALLS IN AMERICA

12/12/93

A MALL AND the NIGHT VISITORS

10/6/94

JIM BORGMAN
"HOMAGE TO GARY LARSON"
CINCINNATI ENQUIRER ©1994
LOST MY JOB IN The FAR SIDE

1/16/92

"WELL, LOOKA HERE..... A STAMP WITH YOUR PICTURE ON IT, PRESLEY."

9/18/88

THE HOSTILE TAKEOVER

7/16/95

JIM BORGMAN
CINCINNATI ENQUIRER ©1995
WHEN MY COMPANY DOWNSIZED I LEARNED TO WORK 14-HOUR DAYS.
I STARTED WORKING HARDER, FASTER, SMARTER, LONGER. INCORPORATED TQM. DID MORE WITH LESS.
TO KEEP UP WITH ALL THE CHANGES I WENT TO WEEKEND SEMINARS, BROUGHT READING HOME EACH NIGHT.
I'M ALWAYS SO BUSY I'VE LOST TRACK OF MY OLD FRIENDS AT WORK.
NOT TO MENTION MY WIFE. SHE WORKS LATE, TOO. DAYCARE IS EATING US ALIVE.
THE KIDS ARE A BLUR. I GET NO EXERCISE. I'M OFF THE STRESS SCALE.
NO MATTER HOW HARD I WORK I'M ALWAYS BEHIND.
BUT, HEY, I CAN'T LET THE CRACKS SHOW.
MY BOSS IS BIG ON TRADITIONAL FAMILY VALUES.

4/29/90

ONCE AGAIN IT'S TIME to ASK MISTER WHIZBANG!
WHAT'S ALL THIS I HEAR ABOUT THE HUBBLE SPACE TELESCOPE?
SIMPLE!
NAMED FOR LANKY NEW YORK GIANTS ACE CARL HUBBELL, THIS POWERFUL TELESCOPE WAS RECENTLY SET IN ORBIT BY ASTRONAUTS ABOARD THE SPACE SHUTTLE DIMAGGIO.
WHEN FULLY OPERATIONAL, ITS LARGE OPTICAL MIRROR WILL UNVEIL TO SCIENTISTS A UNIVERSE ALREADY RENDERED PERMANENTLY INCOMPREHENSIBLE BY STEPHEN HAWKING'S BESTSELLER 'TIME, SPACE, BLACK HOLES, DEATH, JUNK BONDS AND METRIC CONVERSIONS'
JIM BORGMAN
BY ANALYZING SPACE IMAGES HERETOFORE SEEN ONLY IN 'CALVIN AND HOBBES', MANKIND WILL LOOK 14 BILLION YEARS BACKWARD IN TIME TO OUR OWN ORIGIN AS A LIFELESS CHUNK OF SPACE DEBRIS.
Q: HOW?
A: I ALREADY TOLD YOU: WITH MIRRORS.
WITH THE HUBBLE SPACE TELESCOPE, SCIENTISTS WILL NOW SEE TO THE VERY EDGE OF THE UNIVERSE!
WHAT DO YOU MEAN BY 'THE EDGE OF THE UNIVERSE'?
THAT'S WHERE THE, YOU KNOW, STUFF ENDS.
THEN WHAT'S BEYOND THE EDGE OF THE UNIVERSE?
SAY, ISN'T THAT YOUR MOTHER CALLING?
THE IMPLICATIONS ARE STAGGERING!
GEE, Thanks, Mister WHIZBANG!

"DANG! NOW THERE'S AN EYELASH ON THE LENS!"

3/31/92

SEE DICK SMOKE.
SMOKE, DICK, SMOKE.
CIGARETTES
THE TOBACCO INDUSTRY IS SHOCKED -SHOCKED!- AT THE INSINUATION THAT THESE ADS ARE AIMED AT CHILDREN...
JIM BORGMAN CINCINNATI ENQUIRER ©1992

9/16/88

"MAYBE WE SHOULD GET THE BASEMENT CHECKED FOR RADON GAS...... I JUST GOT A CHEST X-RAY FROM CHANGING THE FURNACE FILTER."

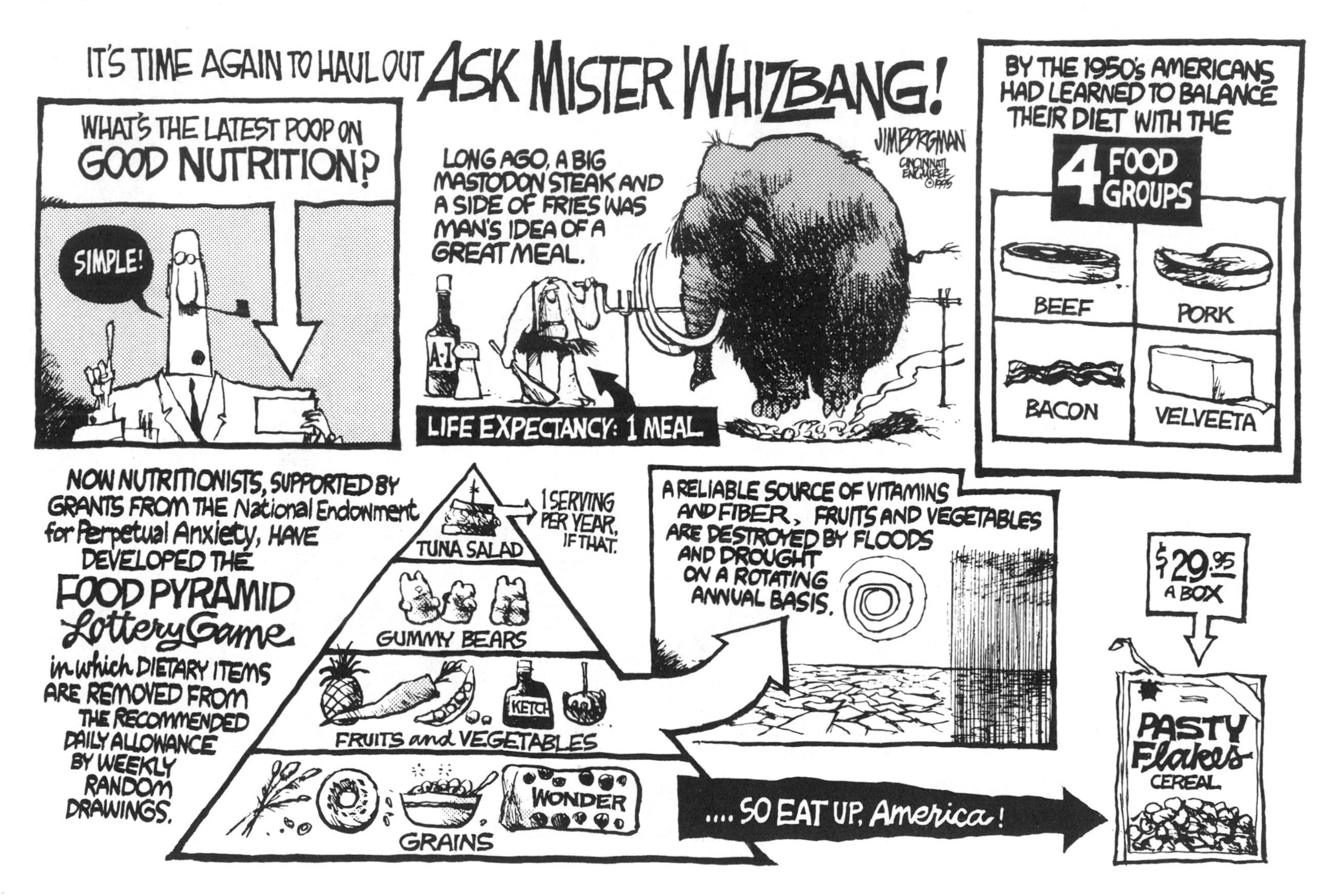
IT'S TIME AGAIN TO HAUL OUT ASK MISTER WHIZBANG!
WHAT'S THE LATEST POOP ON GOOD NUTRITION?
SIMPLE!
LONG AGO, A BIG MASTODON STEAK AND A SIDE OF FRIES WAS MAN'S IDEA OF A GREAT MEAL.
A-1
LIFE EXPECTANCY: 1 MEAL.
JIM BORGMAN
CINCINNATI ENQUIRER ©1995
BY THE 1950's AMERICANS HAD LEARNED TO BALANCE THEIR DIET WITH THE
4 FOOD GROUPS
BEEF
PORK
BACON
VELVEETA
NOW NUTRITIONISTS, SUPPORTED BY GRANTS FROM THE National Endowment for Perpetual Anxiety, HAVE DEVELOPED THE
FOOD PYRAMID Lottery Game
in which DIETARY ITEMS ARE REMOVED FROM THE RECOMMENDED DAILY ALLOWANCE BY WEEKLY RANDOM DRAWINGS.
1 SERVING PER YEAR, IF THAT.
TUNA SALAD
GUMMY BEARS
KETCH
FRUITS and VEGETABLES
WONDER
GRAINS
A RELIABLE SOURCE OF VITAMINS AND FIBER, FRUITS AND VEGETABLES ARE DESTROYED BY FLOODS AND DROUGHT ON A ROTATING ANNUAL BASIS.
$29.95 A BOX
PASTY Flakes CEREAL
.... SO EAT UP, America!

12/2/94

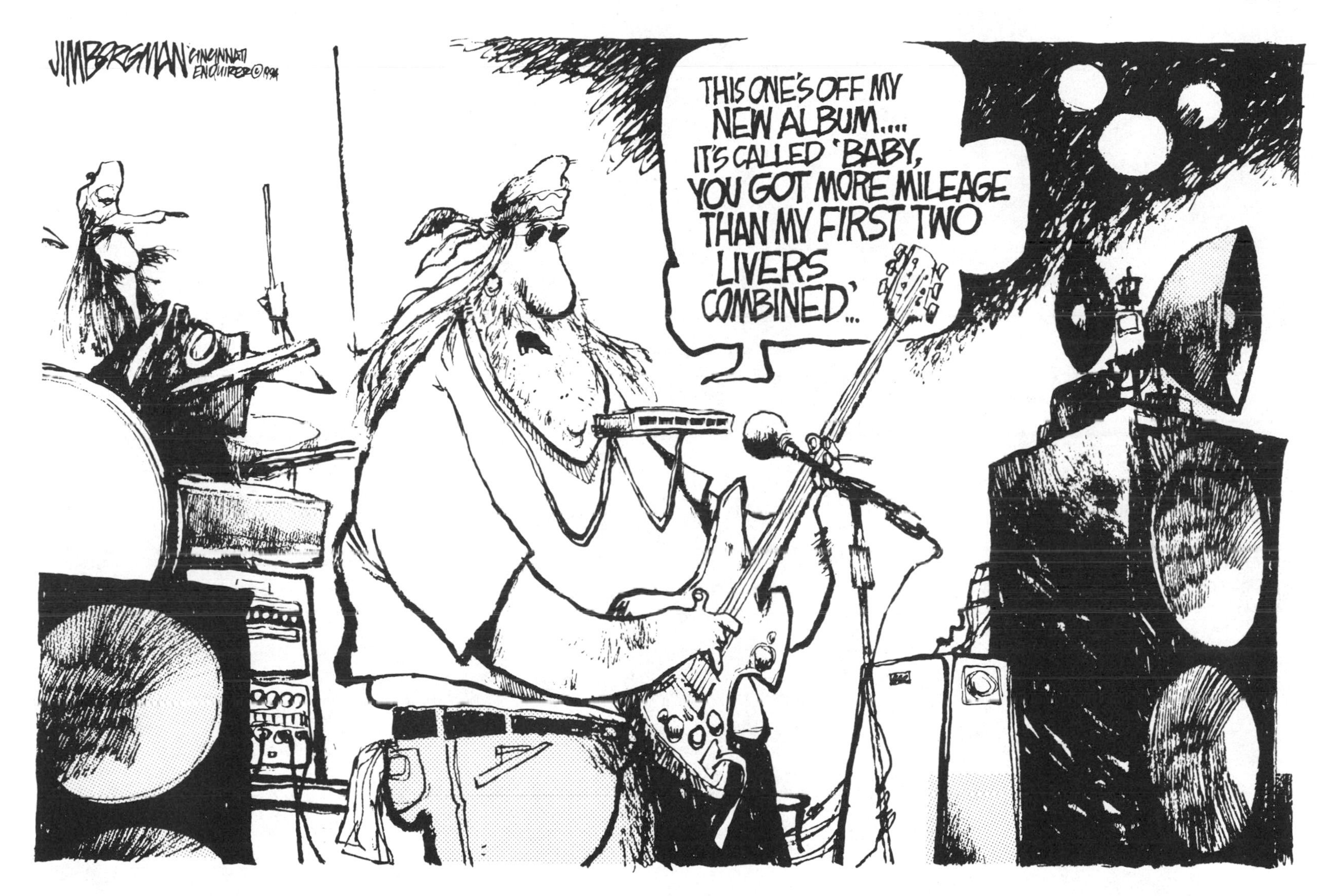
JIM BORGMAN CINCINNATI ENQUIRER ©1994
THIS ONE'S OFF MY NEW ALBUM.... IT'S CALLED 'BABY, YOU GOT MORE MILEAGE THAN MY FIRST TWO LIVERS COMBINED'...

LIVE FROM THE PRESIDENTS SHORTS, IT'S THE NIGHTLY NEWS
WHO IS KEEPING HIM SILENT? THE MAFIA? NO ONE HAS PROVEN OTHERWISE.)
HILLARY WAS HAVING AN AFFAIR WITH ELVIS (THIS WAS COMMON KNOWLEDGE)
AT K-MART WHEN HE GOT OFF WORK.
YECCH!! LET'S JUST PUT IT ALL BACK AND SAY SURGERY WASN'T NECESSARY..
GOP
HEALTH CARE REFORM
JIMMY CARTER
KILLER BUNNY
BUGS BUNNY — ELMER FUDD
NORTH KOREA
KIM IL SUNG
BOSNIA
WHAT'S THE MISSION?
MISSION IMPOSSIBLE
OPERATION RESTORE DEMOCRACY
OPERATION DESERT STORM
OPERATION STORM ~~WINDOWS~~ DOOR
HANG ON, I'M STILL FREE-ASSOCIATING...
DEMOCRACY
HAITI
SOMALIA
MOHAMED FARRAH AIDID
ARISTIDE
ARISTOTLE
ARISTOTLE ONASSIS
RIVAL WARLORDS
PRIMAL SCORECARDS
PAPA DOC
BABY DOC
WHAT'S UP, DOC?
HAITI POLICY:

Troubled Waters

"I FEEL YOUR PAIN."

1/9/94

WHITEWATER EXPEDITIONS
FRANKLY, I DON'T KNOW WHAT THE FUSS IS ALL ABOUT...
MADISON GUARANTY
FOSTER FILES
JIM BORGMAN
CINCINNATI ENQUIRER ©1994

3/13/94

WHITEWATER: What we know for sure so far.....

CINCINNATI ENQUIRER
JIM BORGMAN ©94

VINCENT FOSTER WAS MURDERED BY MR. MUSTARD IN THE WHITE HOUSE DRAWING ROOM WITH A CANDLESTICK.

HIS BODY WAS DUMPED IN A WASHINGTON PARK by ARKANSAS TROOPERS...

...WHO ESCAPED BY UFO!
(RUSH LIMBAUGH ACTUALLY WITNESSED THIS!)

MEANWHILE, A SECOND SHOT RANG OUT FROM A GRASSY KNOLL.

I COULD PROVE IT BUT MY DOG ATE THE MICROFILM.

-OLIVER STONE

HILLARY WAS HAVING AN AFFAIR WITH ELVIS.
(THIS WAS COMMON KNOWLEDGE.)

SHE WOULD MEET HIM AT K-MART WHEN HE GOT OFF WORK.

TO THIS DAY NO ONE WILL ASK HIM ABOUT THIS!!

WHO IS KEEPING HIM SILENT?
THE MAFIA? (NO ONE HAS PROVEN OTHERWISE.)

ACTUAL JOURNALISM
1,000,000 MILES

MORE ON THIS STORY AS ~~RUMORS~~ DETAILS BECOME AVAILABLE.

3/28/94

JIM BORGMAN
CINCINNATI ENQUIRER ©1994
HALE
SHREDDING
STONE-WALLING
TAX ISSUE
RUMORS
CONFLICT OF INTEREST
CREDIBILITY
FOSTER FILES
TREASURY MEETINGS
SUICIDE NOTE
NIBBLED TO DEATH BY DUCKS

5/12/94

JIM BORGMAN CINCINNATI ENQUIRER ©1994
JOCKEY JOCKEY JOCKEY JOCKEY JOCKEY
LIVE FROM THE PRESIDENT'S SHORTS, IT'S THE NIGHTLY NEWS...

4/15/91

JIM BORGMAN CINCINNATI ENQUIRER ©1991
WHO'S THE @☆!#☆@ GENIUS WHO DESIGNED THESE THINGS?!
INSURANCE
MEDICAL COSTS

1/31/94

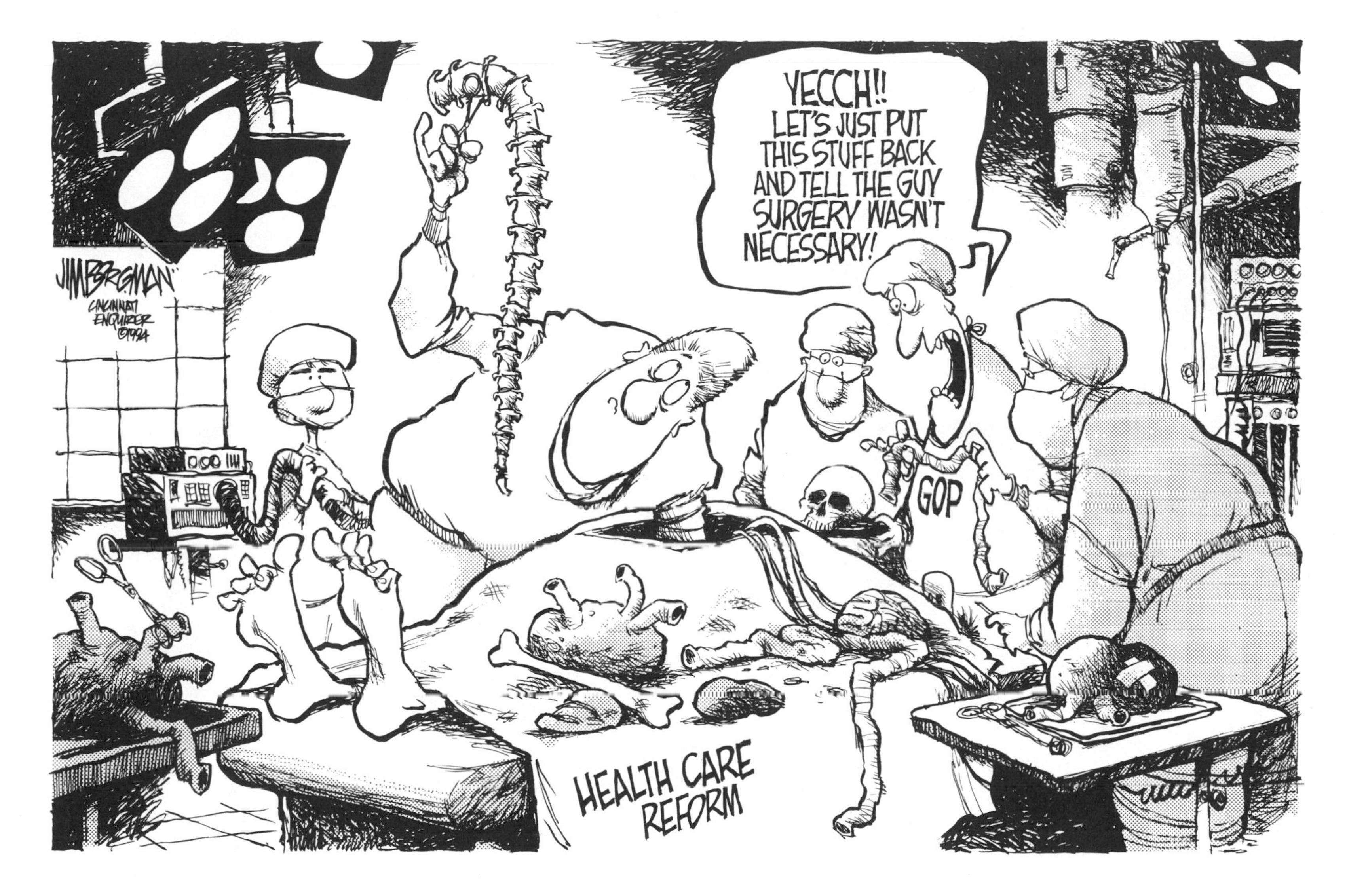

YECCH!! LET'S JUST PUT THIS STUFF BACK AND TELL THE GUY SURGERY WASN'T NECESSARY!
GOP
HEALTH CARE REFORM
JIM BORGMAN
CINCINNATI ENQUIRER ©1994

6/28/94

JIM BORGMAN
CINCINNATI ENQUIRER ©1994
HEALTH REFORM
"LOOK, WE KNOW IT'S HALF-BAKED..... DO YOU ALL WANT PIE OR NOT?"

8/31/94

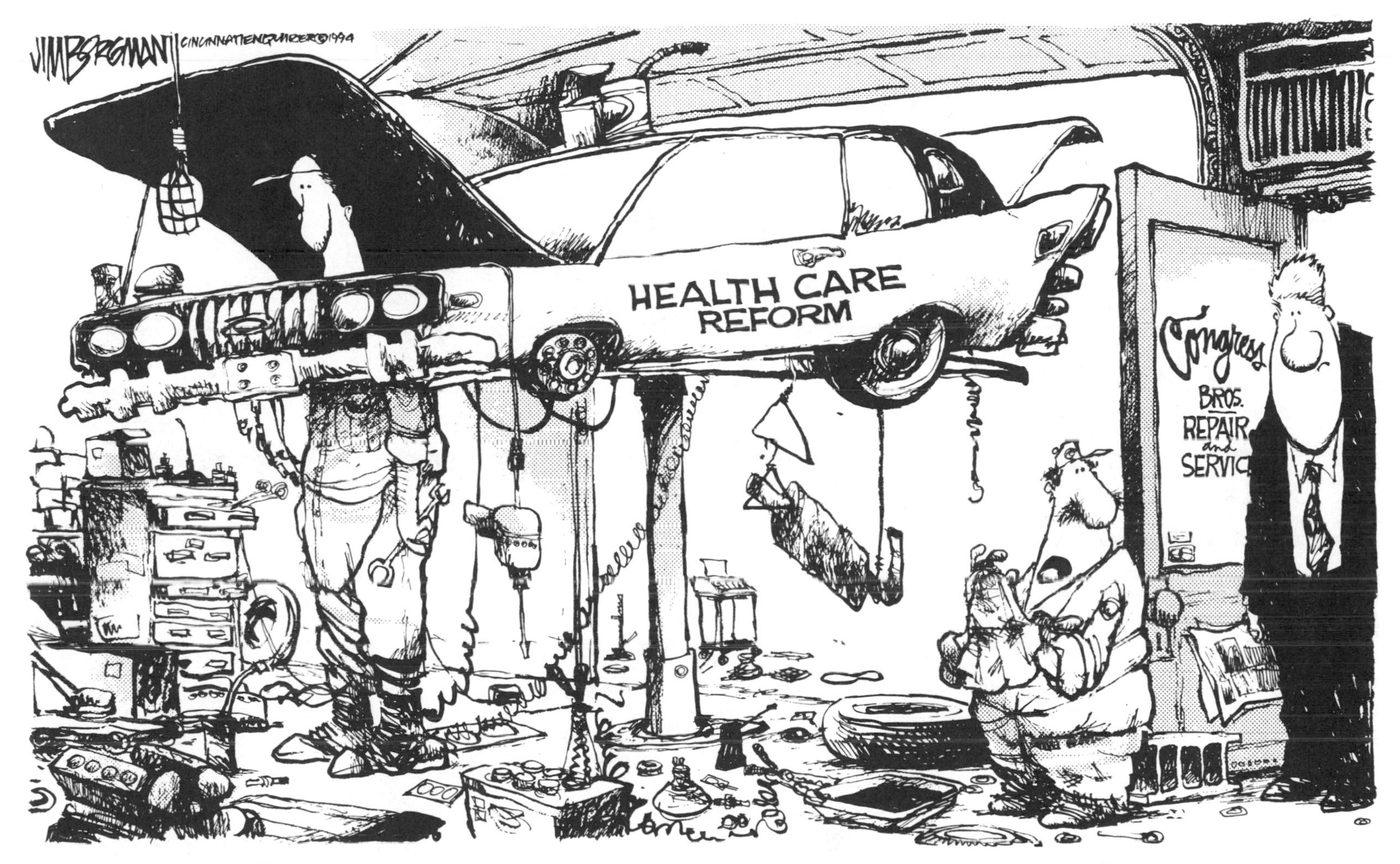

"ON THE BRIGHT SIDE, WE DID GET THOSE ASHTRAYS EMPTIED."

9/27/94

JIM BORGMAN
CINCINNATI ENQUIRER ©1994
CRITICISM
TEFLON
Presidents
CREDIT

10/5/94

JIM BORGMAN
CINCINNATI ENQUIRER ©1994
HANG ON, I'M STILL FREE-ASSOCIATING...
North Korea
KIM IL SUNG
KIM JONG IL
KIM NOVAK
EVANS and NOVAK
BOSNIA
SERBS
SORBETS
RASPBERRY SORBET
RASPBERRY DANIS
William RASPBERR
SOMALIA
Rival Warlord
Klingon Warrior
MISSION CREEP
CREEPY MISSIONARY
PAT
Rwanda
Help Rwanda
Help help me Rhonda
JIMMY CARTER → HUMAN RIGHTS
BILL OF RIGHTS → BILL the CAT → KATMANDU → DALAI LAMA → TIBET
CUBA
CASTRO
CASTROL MOTOR OIL
INDY 500 → FORTUNE 500
CAPITALISM
YELTSIN
Russia
BANANA REPUBLIC →
RETURN PANTS TO BANANA REPUBLIC
WARREN BEATTY →
WARREN CHRISTOPHER
China
Haiti
MOHAMED AIDID
ARISTIDE
ARISTOTLE
ARISTOTLE ONASSIS → GREECE → ZORBA THE GREEK
TONTON MACOUTES → WONTON SOUP
BULL IN A CHINA SHOP →
RUNNING WITH THE BULLS
SPAIN
THONY QUINN →
ANTHONY LAKE →
POST-COLD WAR FOREIGN POLICY:

12/13/94

"...AND NOW, CLASS, A MOMENT OF SILENT PRAYER BEFORE WE BEGIN OUR MASTURBATION LESSON."

10/23/94

" I GIVE UP! THERE'S NOTHING I CAN DO TO THEM THAT THEY HAVEN'T ALREADY DONE TO EACH OTHER. "

10/16/94

Well, WE HAVEN'T GOTTEN RID OF DISEASE, WAR OR PESTILENCE.
BUT THE ECONOMY IS A LOT STRONGER THAN WHEN I TOOK OFFICE.
MORE JOBS WERE CREATED IN THE LAST TWO YEARS than in the FOUR YEARS BEFORE THAT. AND WE'VE CRACKED THE JAPANESE MARKET BIGTIME.
NAFTA LOOKS LIKE A BIG SUCCESS. GATT'S JUST ABOUT PASSED TOO.
WE'RE MAKING PROGRESS ON BRINGING the DEFICIT DOWN FOR THE FIRST TIME IN DECADES, AHEAD OF OUR SCHEDULE.
The BRADY BILL IS LAW. ASSAULT WEAPONS ARE BANNED.
WE'RE GETTING THOSE VACANT FEDERAL JUDGESHIPS FILLED WITH QUALIFIED PEOPLE and WE HAVE TWO SOLID SUPREME COURT JUSTICES.
FOR THE FIRST TIME IN YEARS WE HAVE SOME LEADERSHIP ON RACIAL ISSUES COMING FROM THE WHITE HOUSE.
WE BROUGHT THE HEALTH CARE DEBATE TO THE FRONT BURNER AND THRASHED IT OUT AS PROMISED.
RUSSIA, NORTHERN IRELAND, the MIDDLE EASTERN NATIONS AND SOUTH AFRICA ALL CREDIT US WITH HELPING IN THEIR TRANSFORMATIONS.
OUR HAITI PLAN IS WORKING. DEMOCRACY'S GOT A CHANCE. CEDRAS IS GONE.
IRAQ GOT OUR MESSAGE. SADDAM BLINKED. EVEN THE JORDANIANS SIGNED ON TO THE PROGRAM.
JIM BORGMAN
CINCINNATI ENQUIRER ©1994
....SO I GUESS IT HASN'T BEEN A TOTAL LOSS.
FAMILY LEAVE
NATIONAL SERVICE
PROGRAM
NORTH ...
1oz
YOU THINK I'M GIVING YOU ONE OUNCE OF CREDIT FOR THAT ?!! HA!
HOW ABOUT THAT BIMBO IN ARKANSAS?! COUNTRY'S GONE DOWN THE TUBES EVER SINCE!!!

12/11/94

PUT UP
PUT UP
PUT UP
PUT UP
OH, SHOT UP
POWER TO THE STATES! WE WANT ACCOUNTABILITY!
LET WHO KNOW HOW I FEEL?
YOU DON'T KNOW? WHAT DISTRICT ARE YOU IN? WHO'S YOUR STATE SENATOR, THEN?
I FORGET HER NAME IT MIGHT BEGIN WITH A "B"... OR "M"...
CAN YOU FIND YOUR STATE CAPITOL BUILDING WITH TWO HANDS? WHEN WERE YOU THERE LAST? WHEN ARE THEY IN SESSION? EVER WATCH THEM ON
WE DID A FIELD TRIP IN 8TH GRADE...
OH, DON'T YOU JUST HATE IT WHEN THEY PRESS THEIR NOSES AGAINST THE GLASS CEILING AND LOOK AT YOU LIKE THAT?
MOM! A NEWT ATE KERMIT THE FROG!
WHITE GUYS STILL RULE
RACIAL

You Say You Want a Devolution

ANOTHER ATTACK LAUNCHED ON WHITE HOUSE

11/25/94

JIM BORGMAN ©CINCINNATI ENQUIRER ©1994
AGENDA
YOU WANT FRIES WITH THAT?
BILL
GOP
Land of NEWT

1/13/95

"...AND YES, WE MUST CONTINUE TO EXPLORE NEW WAYS TO GENERATE REVENUE."

11/22/94

NEWTIES
BUT I HAVE TONED DOWN MY RHETORIC...!
JIM BORGMAN
CINCINNATI ENQUIRER ©1994

2/17/95

SO YOU'VE HAD ENOUGH OF BIG GOVERNMENT, HUH?
POWER TO THE STATES! WE WANT ACCOUNT-ABILITY!
GREAT. START WITH WELFARE. LET THEM KNOW HOW YOU FEEL.
LET WHO KNOW HOW I FEEL?
WELL, YOUR STATE REPRESENTATIVE, FOR ONE.
AND THAT WOULD BE.....?
YOU DON'T KNOW? WHAT DISTRICT ARE YOU IN? OK THEN, WHO'S YOUR STATE SENATOR?
I FORGET HER NAME... IT MIGHT BEGIN WITH 'B'.....OR 'M'...
CAN YOU FIND YOUR STATEHOUSE WITH BOTH HANDS? WHEN WERE YOU THERE LAST? WHEN ARE THEY IN SESSION? EVER WATCH THEM ON CABLE? WASN'T THERE A BIG SCANDAL THERE LAST YEAR? WHAT WAS THAT ALL ABOUT?
WE MADE A FIELD TRIP IN 8TH GRADE...
SO THIS IS ACCOUNTABILITY?
SWEARTOGOD I'LL VOTE THEM OUT IF I FIND OUT WHO THEY ARE!!
WELCOME TO DEVOLUTION

5/17/95

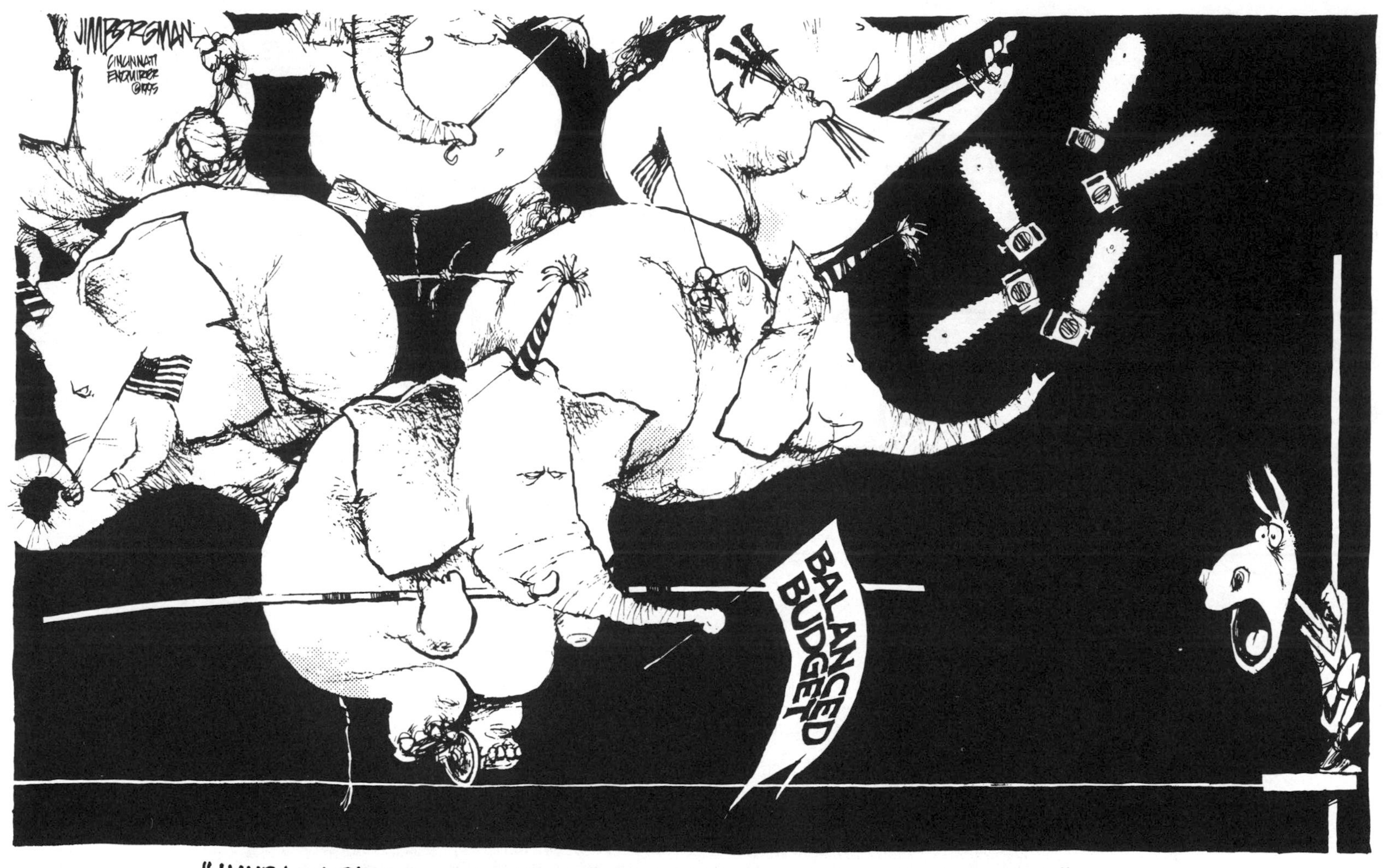

"HAVE YOU EVER ONCE CONSIDERED WHAT THIS IS DOING TO MY SELF-ESTEEM?"

2/21/95

SQUEALING LIKE A STUCK PIG

12/28/94

NEW YEARS RESOLUTION #1: RECONSIDER THE FLAT TAX

3/12/95

THE FLATTER THE BETTER

4/28/95

LIBERATED FROM THE SHACKLES OF WELFARE ENSLAVEMENT AND EMBRACED BY A SPIRIT OF TOUGH LOVE, POOR AMERICANS ARE SET FREE TO FLY.

(FLIGHT TRAINING, HOWEVER, WAS DEEMED TOO COSTLY FOR THE CURRENT BUDGET.)

3/25/94

JIMBORGMAN
CINCINNATI ENQUIRER ©1994
BUT IT'S HOT IN THERE!!
KITCHEN

2/12/95

THAT WASN'T SO BAD!
1996 BUDGET
SPENDING CUTS
Congress
HEAVY LIFTING
JIM BORGMAN
CINCINNATI ENQUIRER ©1995

6/8/95

PUT UP
PUT UP
PUT UP
PUT UP
PUT UP
PUT UP
OH, SHUT UP!
JIM BORGMAN
CINCINNATI ENQUIRER ©1995

12/22/93

JIMBORGMAN
CINCINNATI ENQUIRER©1993
WHEN DID WE ALL BEGIN VOTING ON EACH OTHER'S RIGHTS, ANYWAY?
GAY RIGHTS VOTED UP, DOWN, RECONSIDERED, OVERTURNE
COLORADO #2, ISSUE 3, etc.

6/25/95

RACIAL PREFERENCES ARE UNFAIR
GEE, THEY WORKED OK FOR THE 376 YEARS THEY PREFERRED YOU.
JIM BORGMAN CINCINNATI ENQUIRER ©1995

3/10/95

IT'S TRUE... WE SHOULD BE REGULARLY RE-EXAMINING THE NEED FOR THESE PROGRAMS.
HERE COMES THE REVISION COMMITTEE NOW.
AFFIRMATIVE ACTION
JIMBORGMAN
CINCINNATI ENQUIRER ©1995

3/21/95

JIM BORGMAN CINCINNATI ENQUIRER ©1995
OH, DON'T YOU JUST HATE IT WHEN THEY PRESS THEIR NOSES AGAINST THE GLASS CEILING AND LOOK AT YOU LIKE THAT?...
WHITE GUYS STILL RULE

9/23/94

"MOMMY, WHERE DO DADDIES COME FROM?"

4/21/95

"....ON THE BRIGHT SIDE, THE ENDANGERED SPECIES LIST IS DOWN TO ONE."

GOOD DICK
BAD DICK
"CANCEL MY APPOINTMENTS... THIS ONE MAY TAKE AWHILE."
MEDIA
O.J. STORY
"IT'S NOT JUST FOR BREAKFAST ANY
FREEZE! Internet Police!
SURE I FEEL A LITTLE TWINGE INSIDE BUT IT'S FROM THE ELECTRODES THE TRILATERAL COMMISSION IMPLAN
Richard Nixon
I WISH THEY'D NEVER STARTED ALL THIS TALK ABOUT
"THEY GOT OWEN ALL CHARGED UP WITH THIS TALK OF REPLACEMENT

This Just In...

TOO MUCH COURT TV...

7/3/94

"IT ISN'T JUST FOR BREAKFAST ANYMORE!"

6/25/94

JIM BORGMAN CINCINNATI ENQUIRER ©1994
Newsweek
Simpson
TIME
Simpson
JOURNALISM TODAY
Simpson
Real
Altered
Really Altered

2/15/91

JIM BORGMAN
CINCINNATI ENQUIRER ©1991
...PLUS, WE WANT TWELVE BUCKS FOR HIS AUTOGRAPH ON THE BOTTOM OF THE CONTRACT.

1/24/92

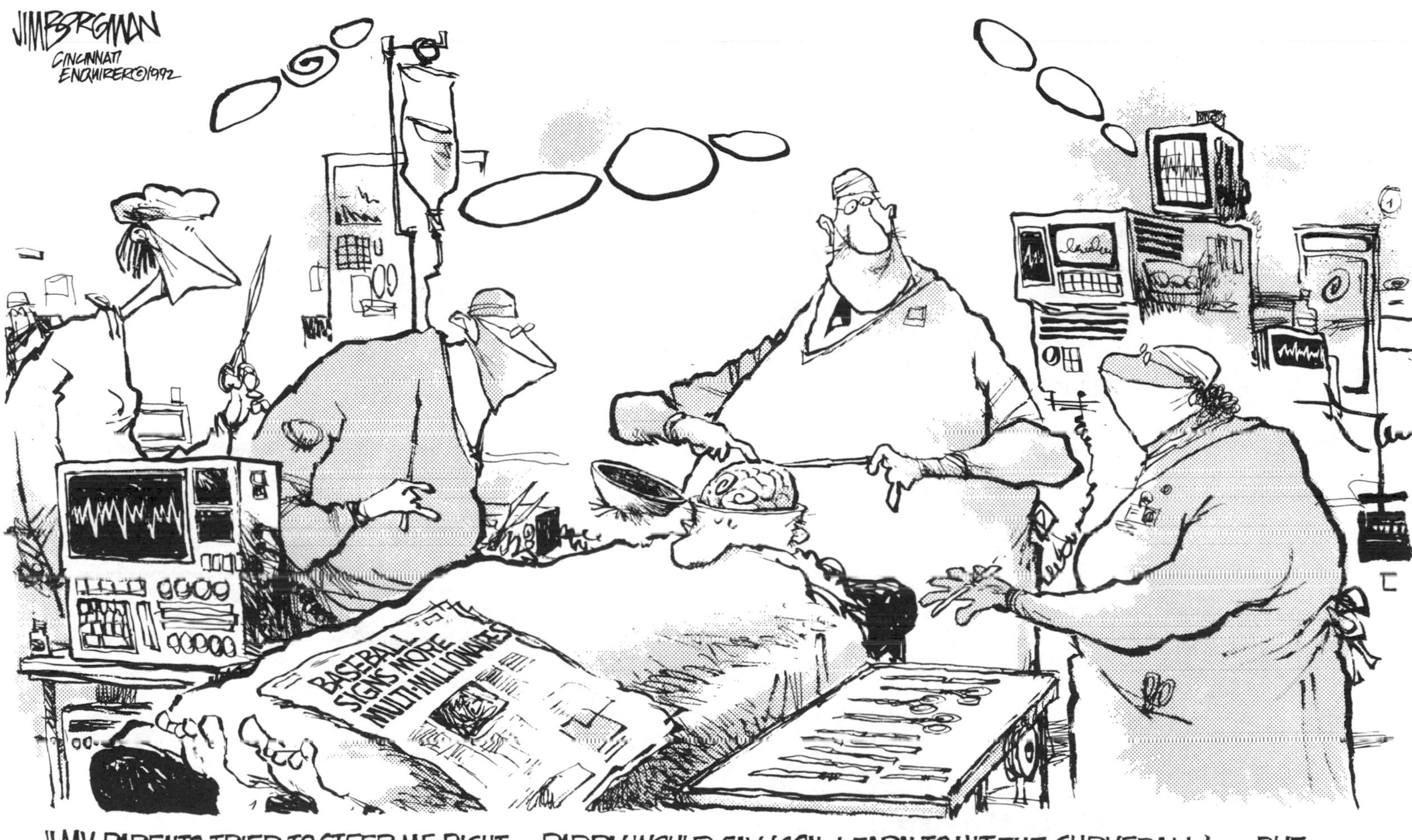

"MY PARENTS TRIED TO STEER ME RIGHT..... DADDY WOULD SAY, 'SON, LEARN TO HIT THE CURVEBALL'..... BUT NOOOOOO, I HAD TO GO OFF AND BECOME A BRAIN SURGEON!"

9/15/94

JIM BORGMAN
CINCINNATI ENQUIRER ©1994
BUY YOUR OWN DAM' GREY POUPON!
OWNERS
PLAYERS

8/21/94

2/10/95

JIM BORGMAN
CINCINNATI ENQUIRER ©1995
Mudville
1
LINEUP
BATS

8/17/94

BASEBALL STRIKE WEEK ONE:
PLAYERS GET REACQUAINTED WITH THE WORKING WORLD

3/8/95

" THIS BASEBALL STRIKE IS PATHETIC..... NOW THE PLAYERS HAVE HIRED REPLACEMENT WHINERS. "

7/2/95

"KEEP TRYING, TOMMY...... THERE'S NO TIME TO DRAFT A CONSTITUTIONAL AMENDMENT BEFORE KICKOFF."

9/8/94

"WOMEN'S RIGHTS. WOMEN'S HEALTH. ALWAYS THEY'VE GOT TO BRING WOMEN INTO IT."

4/23/94

"CANCEL MY APPOINTMENTS..... THIS ONE MAY TAKE AWHILE."

1/24/95

STUCK IN A GO-NOWHERE, SECOND-WAVE JOB, EH MAC?
MALGAMATED CARBONIC WINGNUT INC.
UH...
WELL, WAKE UP AND SMELL THE CAPPUCCINO! AMERICANS DON'T MAKE STUFF ANYMORE.
KA-CHUNK
THIS IS THE INFORMATION AGE. WHADJA, SLEEP THROUGH NAFTA?
WELL, I.....
RAM
SO SHIP THAT JOB TO SINGAPORE AND CLIMB ABOARD THE THIRD WAVE!
IS THERE A BOWLING TEAM?
PROGRAM YOUR ANSWERING MACHINE FROM YOUR MICRO-WAVE
ORDER BUFFALO WINGS ON YOUR HARD DRIVE
YOUR COFFEEMAKER IS ALSO A FAX MACHINE
MODEM ALLOWS YOUR FONDUE POT TO TALK DIRECTLY TO YOUR SALAD SHOOTER
LISTEN TO CD's ON YOUR BEEPER

2/14/95

"MY DOG ATE THE DISK MY HOMEWORK WAS ON."

2/1/87

6/4/95

ONE STORY ABOUT BEING WHITE
JIM BORGMAN CINCINNATI ENQUIRER ©1995
I REMEMBER LOOKING FOR MY FIRST APARTMENT WHEN I CAME BACK HOME AFTER COLLEGE.
THERE WAS THIS PLACE DOWN BY THE RIVER, HALF OF A DUPLEX, THAT WAS KIND OF NICE.
WHEN I SAT DOWN WITH THE LANDLADY TO TALK ABOUT THE DETAILS, SHE SAID SOMETHING THAT MADE MY HEART LODGE IN MY THROAT
I'M GLAD TO RENT TO A NICE MAN LIKE YOU INSTEAD OF, YOU KNOW, ONE OF THE COLOREDS.
I REMEMBER THAT I JUST SAT THERE, DIDN'T SAY ANYTHING, JUST STARTED LOOKING FOR THE FASTEST WAY TO GET OUT OF THERE AND NEVER COME BACK.
I REMEMBER BEING POLITE AND HATING MYSELF FOR IT.
I THINK IT WAS BECAUSE SHE HAD JUST CALLED ME A 'NICE MAN.'
I'VE ALWAYS WISHED I'D TOLD HER, 'I WON'T RENT FROM YOU EITHER.' THEN STOOD UP AND WALKED OUT.
JUST STAND UP AND WALK OUT, MAN. JUST STAND UP AND WALK OUT.
I'VE PRACTICED THAT SCENE IN MY MIND OVER AND OVER SINCE THEN.
BUT RACISM DOESN'T SEEM TO COME AT ME STRAIGHT ON LIKE THAT ANYMORE. IT'S ALWAYS CAMOUFLAGED AND BETWEEN THE LINES, AND I'M A BLOCK AWAY BEFORE I RECOGNIZE WHAT IT WAS.
ONE THING I AM STRAIGHT ABOUT, THOUGH....
I DON'T WANT TO BE A 'NICE MAN' ANYMORE.

7/7/95

JIM BORGMAN ©CINCINNATI ENQUIRER ©1995
BLACK-ON-BLACK VIOLENCE.
THE LIGHT SHED ON IT.
THE CONCERN SHOWN ABOUT IT.
THE WILLINGNESS TO DEAL WITH IT.

7/28/95

IT TAKES A WHOLE VILLAGE TO RAISE A CHILD.
BUT THE VILLAGE IS ON CRACK.
THE VILLAGE IS RULED BY GANGS.
THE VILLAGE DOESN'T KNOW IT'S A VILLAGE.
AND THE CHILDREN AREN'T CHILDREN ANYMORE.
JIM BORGMAN
CINCINNATI ENQUIRER ©1995

2/4/94

4/25/94

JIM BORGMAN
CINCINNATI ENQUIRER ©1994
UNDER CONSTRUCTION
New
SERBIAN WING

7/23/95

BLOODBATH

7/31/94

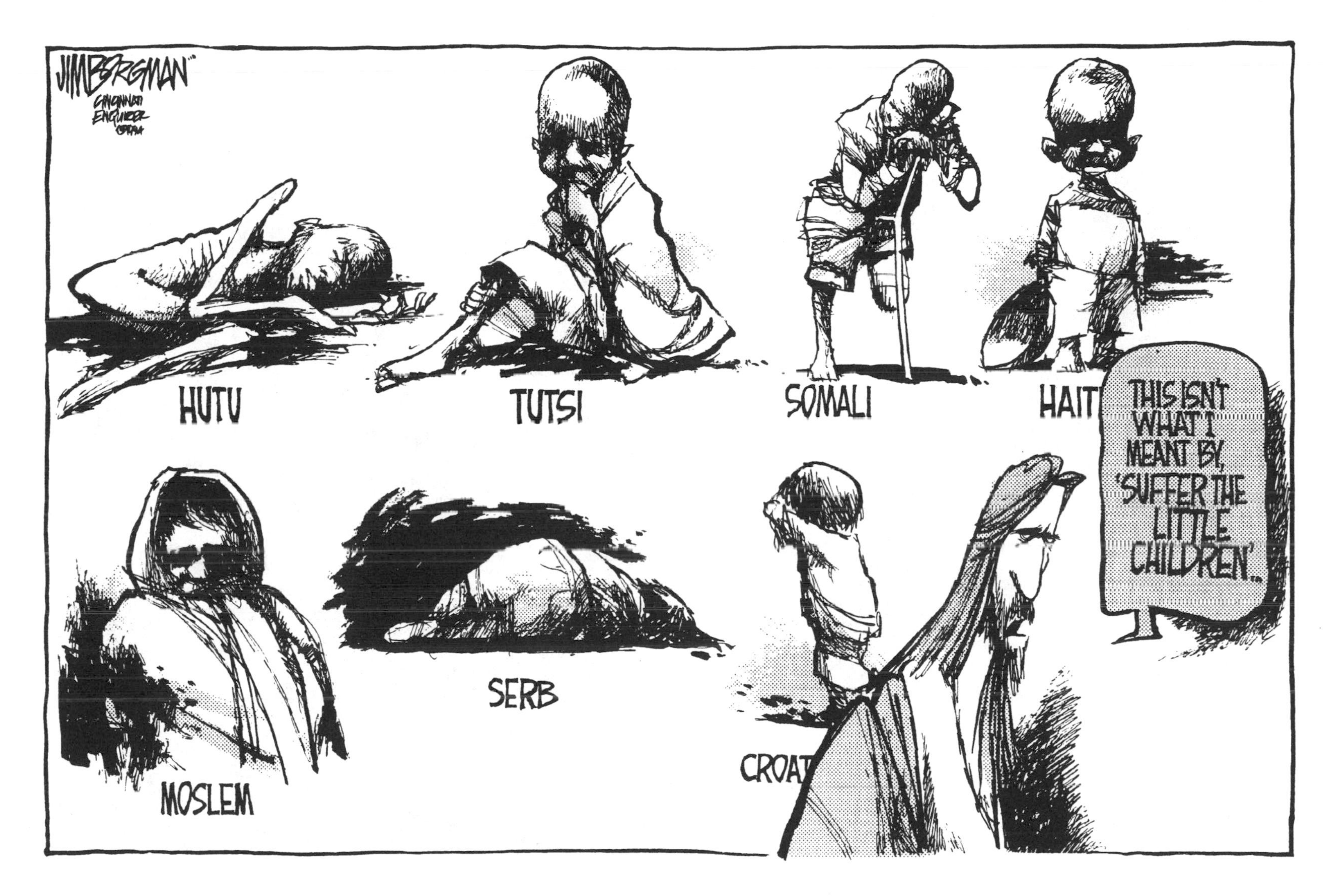
JIM BORGMAN
HUTU
TUTSI
SOMALI
HAIT
MOSLEM
SERB
CROAT
THIS ISN'T WHAT I MEANT BY, 'SUFFER THE LITTLE CHILDREN'...

4/20/95

JIM BORGMAN
CINCINNATI ENQUIRER ©1995
APROPOS OF NOTHING, I WONDER HOW THE NUCLEAR PROLIFERATION TALKS ARE GOING....?
OKLA

4/23/95

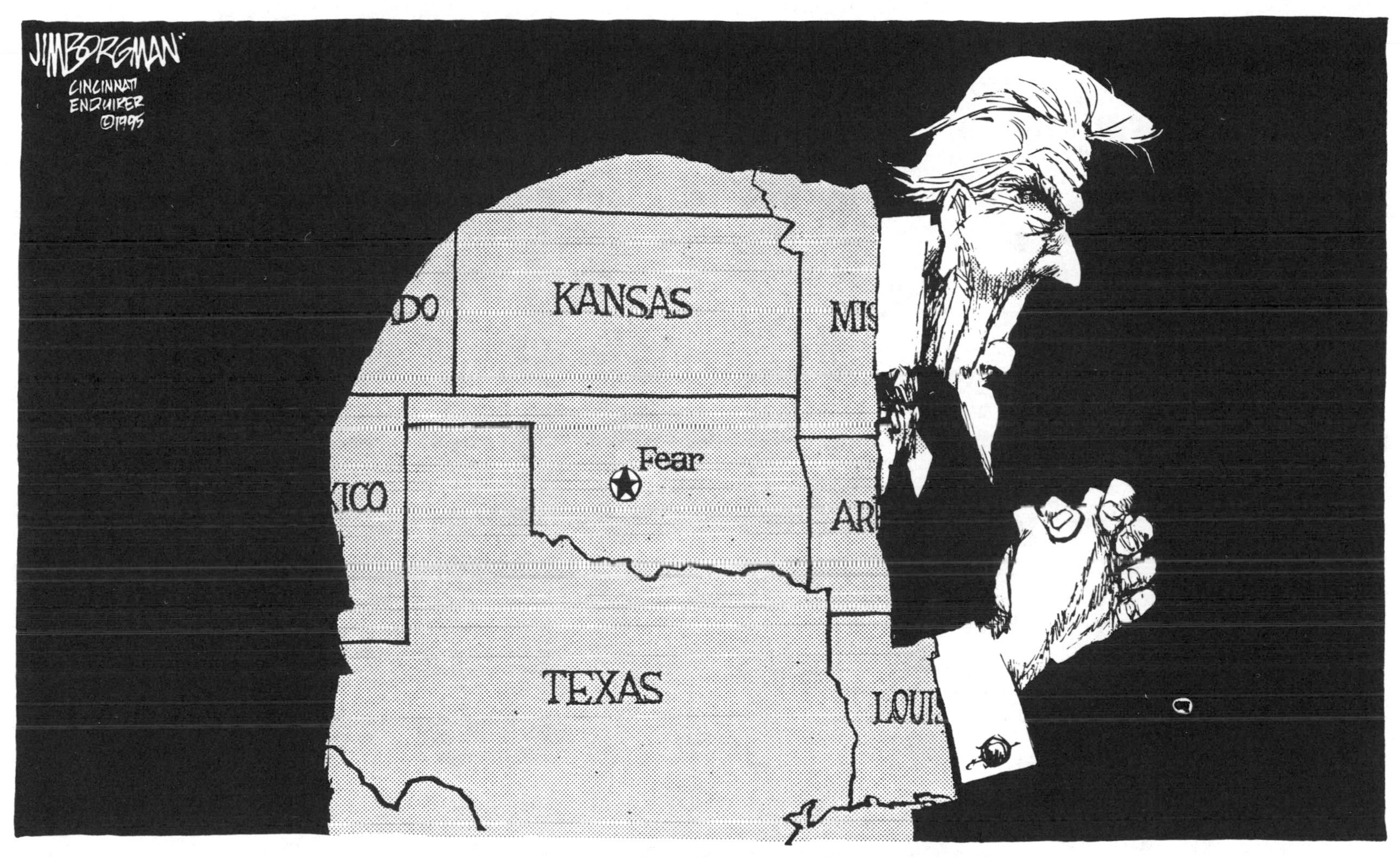

IN THE HEART OF THE HEART OF THE COUNTRY

5/10/95

JIM BORGMAN
America's MILITIAS DO SOME SOUL SEARCHING
SURE I FEEL A LITTLE TWINGE INSIDE SOMETIMES....
BUT IT'S JUST FROM THE ELECTRODES THE TRILATERAL COMMISSION IMPLANTED IN MY GALL BLADDER.
MOM
OKLAHOMA CITY AFTERMATH

5/11/95

"..... AND THEY WONDER WHY WE'RE DISGRUNTLED."

7/30/95

Ode to a Typewriter

I've clattered for days on my new PC
With nary a filled-in o or e.
Perhaps it's time to show the door
To this qwertyuiop dinosaur.

You've offered me no font choice yet,
No surfing on no Internet,
No e-mail sites, no cybermall,
You never fax, you never call.

With you I've never been online
Unless you count the underline.
Not once did you offer me Nexis or Lexis,
Just Wite-out smears and strings of XXXXXs.

And yet my thoughts poured 'tween your tabs,
You never bombed, you never crabbed.
No little clock whirls while you pause.
You never asked me to learn DOS.

No memory to weigh you down,
(My hard drive wears a constant frown.)
Now swallowed by time like a latter-day Jonah
I bid farewell to my old Smith Corona.

7/12/95

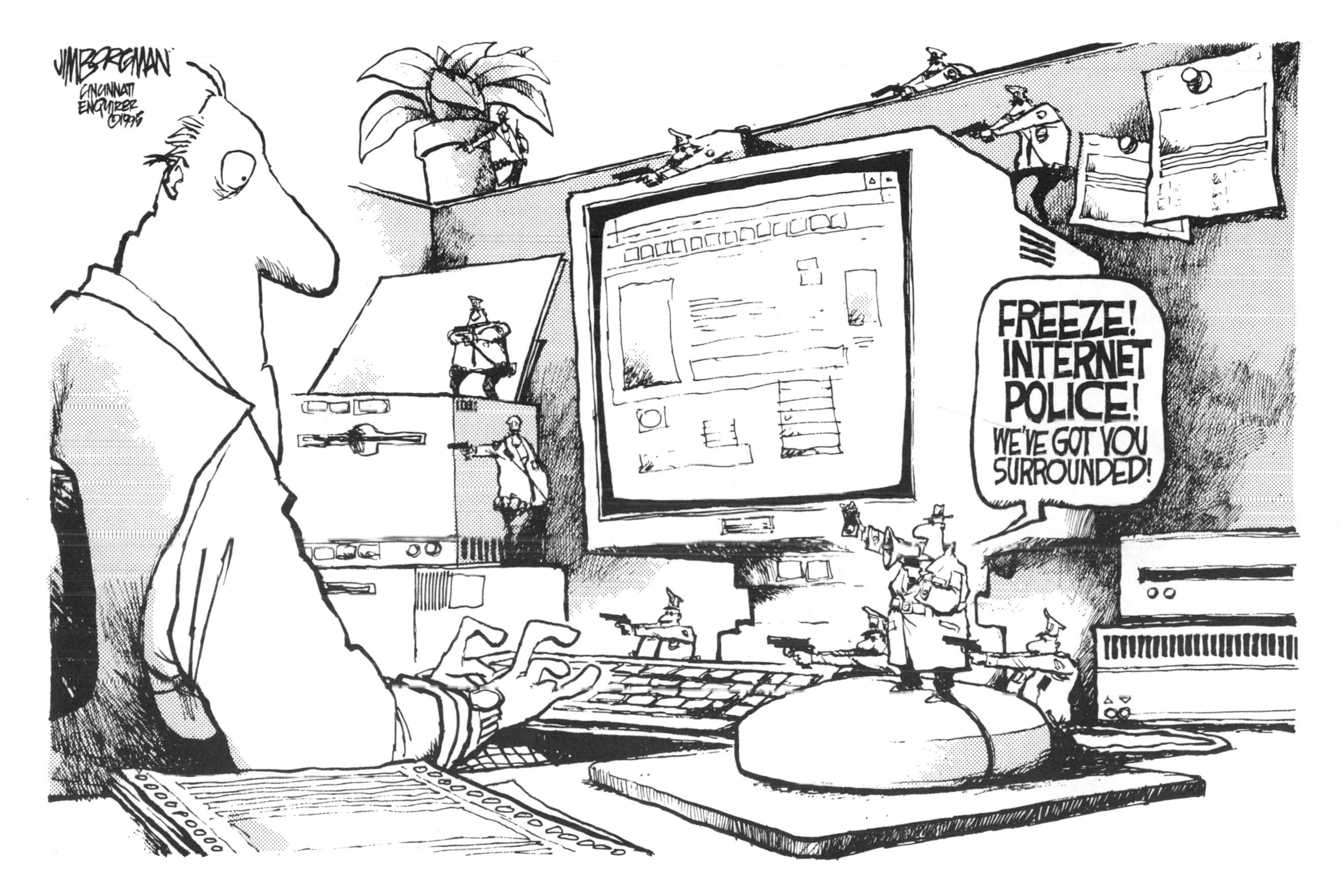
JIM BORGMAN
CINCINNATI ENQUIRER ©1995
FREEZE! INTERNET POLICE! WE'VE GOT YOU SURROUNDED!

3/29/95

"AND IF I EVER CATCH YOU DOWNLOADING DIRTY PICTURES FROM THE INTERNET AGAIN, YOUNG MAN, I'LL WASH YOUR MOUSE OUT WITH SOAP!"

10/4/95

JIM BORGMAN
CINCINNATI ENQUIRER ©1995
HOW AM I EVER SUPPOSED TO TRUST YOU AGAIN?
WHITE AMERICA
O.J. WALKS
BEEN THERE
BLACK AMERICA

8/8/95